Laminitis

An Equine Plague of
Unconscionable Proportions

Healing and Protecting Your Horse
Using Natural Principles and Practices

Jaime Jackson

Author, *The Natural Horse:*
Lessons from the Wild

NHC Press

For further information:

NHC Press — an imprint of J. Jackson Publishing
P.O. Box 1432
Lompoc, CA 93436
NHCPressInfo@gmail.com
805-735-8480

ISBN-10: 0-9848399-3-3
ISBN-13: 978-0-9848399-3-3

Laminitis is a serious, potentially life-threatening disease. Neither the author nor NHC Press accept responsibility for the applications or misapplications of recommendations given in this book. Horse owners should always consult first with their professional natural hoof care and holistic veterinary providers.

Primum non nocere . . . vis medicatrix naturale.

First, do no harm . . . (respect) the healing powers of nature.

– Hippocrates (5th Century BC)

CONTENTS

§

List of Tables

The mind-boggling levels and ever-widening spread of laminitis among all breeds of equines and in all disciplines around the world defy quantification. In my own clinics, it is nearly impossible to find cadavers that do not bear the mark of laminitis to some degree — and I have been conducting these for over 20 years. It is virtually impossible to visit a boarding facility, barn or pasture where its symptoms are not evident. As a plague of unconscionable proportions relative to the number horses on this planet, it has settled upon the horse world and, casting its grisly pall, clenches horse and owner firmly in its devastating grip. Yet, as a global epidemic, few owners recognize the extent of what is happening and why. So the plague continues its insidious spread under the radar of an unsuspecting horse world. *How, in heaven's name, is this possible?*

First off, the science and proven practices of natural horse/hoof care (NHC), based on the wild horse model, have made clear the causes, cure, and prevention of laminitis. And this book provides a concise and useful guide for horse owners to take immediate and swift action against laminitis and keep it out of their horses' lives once and for all. Which is to say that the disease actually has its remedy and preventative "vaccine" within the regime of NHC. Like polio, it should be a thing of the past. But, as I've said, the plague is very much alive and rampaging, and it truly is a globally burgeoning and onerous burden upon the horse using community. The question many of us operating within the "safety zone" of NHC are asking is, "why?"

I ask to the point, what is the basis for this growing and unnecessary debacle, and what is sustaining it exactly? I've pondered this enigma for years, watching the plague *grow and grow and grow*. To me, it is almost surreal, as though it is a bizarre and acceptable cultural phenomena, born somehow of a defunct moral compass in which "treating symptoms" — which is typically today's status quo — is superior to prevention or eliminating the cause altogether. Given the levels of equine suffering, I can't think of a more disconcerting and vexing image of human failure. Horse owners, firmly ensconced in their micro-cultures according to discipline, seemingly accept it, "whatever it [the plague] is", and treat its symptoms the best they can within their cultural mindsets. Vets, farriers, and pharmaceutical companies, in turn, cater to their needs by providing a galaxy of variant and contradictory products and practices aimed exclusively at treating symptoms. Discussions of "causality" are marginalized or given to speculation, bogus science, and even ego-driven anger should a horse owner actually press their vet or farrier to address causality in a way that makes sense. For those brave enough to buck the system, and really put on the full court press for an answer, they will soon find themselves on the Internet looking for "outsiders" like myself in hopes of getting a straight answer. But even at the fringe of conventional care, particularly on the Internet, lies a tangled web of nonsense, confusion and contradictory advice administered by hordes of self-proclaimed "experts" and others saying anything and everything about "what to do" and without a shred of evidence, accountability or verifiable expertise. For horse owners wanting and needing good information, the search can be frustrating and daunting with potentially treacherous outcomes for the horse if they fall victim to a smooth-talking predator. So, *can something really be done?* Actually, yes, and the answer lies in a logical — although unrecognized — explanation for the plague in the first place. And I'll come right to it: the disease is, in fact, an enormous profiteering racket that feeds the voracious appetite of what can only be called a "laminitis industry". This industry counts on horse owners being ill-informed and basically doing what their equally ill-informed service providers tell them to do.

This evil axis of the plague is vast but well-defined and distinctly linear in construct — if one only stops long enough to think about it, investigate its components, and connect the dots that lie between them: veterinary medicine in the field, veterinary hospitals, corrective shoeing, horseshoe manufacturers, trade schools, universities and university research, drugs, agribusiness, government regulators, banks, humane associations, and even law enforcement! We are talking about enormous profits, in the range of billions of dollars that are derived from the laminitis debacle to feed and sustain its investors, manufacturers, and workers right on down the line. There is so much laminitis money conducted along this unyielding chain of beneficiaries I would liken it now to the "banks too big to fail" financial conundrum facing every sector of society in the world today. If one link fails, the whole industry is imperiled. This doesn't seem likely, however, so long as people remain ignorant of laminitis causality, and proven holistic pathways to healing are obscured or denigrated by wanton profiteering at all costs.

Ever the optimist, I think this "axis of profiteering" may, ironically, have its place. But not in its current destructive incarnation. The alternative, if you will, lies in "feeding" the parallel axis of NHC — holistic care based on the wild horse model (Chapter 11) — which favors soundness and vitality, not profits for profit's sake and the horse be damned. Nipping away at the edges of the plague is a burgeoning NHC movement of advocates, practitioners, and awakened horse owners who want nothing more than what is good for their horses. This is a significant and important pivot away from profiteering at all costs and that bodes well for the horse and the owner's pocketbook. As it stands now, it is the horse owner who shoulders the financial burden that feeds the laminitis money trail, and the horse who pays the ultimate price. So, the solution lies not in a drug addicted world of "treating symptoms" but in the holistic fold of equine *vitality*. There is no shortage of things that we all can, and should, do to support this end: more responsible horse ownership, good science, good research, safe feeds, safe drugs, and a revolutionary new vanguard of allied services that inure to the healthful vitality of the horse, not a perpetual state of laminitis. But we'll never see any of it if we persist in the delusion that the current stream of "profits at all costs" — the industrialization of laminitis — equates to the well-being of the horse. It doesn't, and the intent of this book is to show why while pointing to a good path to get ourselves and our horses on at very little expense.

§

I would be remiss as an advocate for humane animal care if I didn't broadened the circle of the industrialized food chain to include other domesticated species afflicted no differently than the horse. I have visited hog confinement operations where laminitis is so prevalent that suffering breeding stock have to be slaughtered like clockwork because they can barely walk. Dairy cows and cattle in feed lots suffer nearly the same fate. A USDA agent I know once told me that close-confined chickens practically "explode" internally from metabolic breakdown due to force-feeding of feeds laced with laminitis triggers. Ungulates in zoos are also victims, which I have seen also with my own eyes. Even elephants in circus sideshows don't escape the plague.

In 1989, I was attending the American Farriers Association's annual cnference held at John Ascuaga's Nugget Casino in Sparks, Nevada. As darkness fell, a few of us ventured outside to get a breath of fresh air. Standing just outside the building in the parking area, our attention was sud-

denly a taken by the grating sound of an enormous metal roller door opening before our very eyes. What the . . . . ? A moment later, out came a huge female elephant (her name was "Bertha") making loud clanging sounds with each foot step. As "hoof men," we instinctively ignored the billboards hanging off each side of her and focused on her feet. Chained to them were these enormous metal plates, which resembled flat "baking pans." I recall one of the farriers saying, "Look, she's got laminitis." The tell-tale symptoms of chronic laminitis were evident as we stepped to look closer. Bertha, captured in India in 1945, died in 1999, advertised as "a member of the Nugget family." When not performing, she lived in a paddock in the Nugget's parking lot. Official cause of death: "Old age and complications from arthritis." Arthritis? Then, as now, laminitis was very much misunderstood. A bit shaken, we returned to the conference hall as Bertha was led down the main avenue to pitch the casino — an indelible memory left with at least some of us, I'm certain.

But, in all such instances, we find the same triggered-up feeds produced and supported by the same long chain of profiteers we see in the horse world. Given that many of these species are part of our own food chain, are we not wise to ponder the implications of laminitis in relation to our own health? In fact, these are sick animals that are infected, contaminated, and hosting strains of bacteria — and very likely predator viruses suited to their environment — that belong in no living creature.

Jaime Jackson
Lompoc, CA/USA
June/2016

Chapter One

What is Laminitis?

There are a number of definitions for laminitis floating around in the horse world today. The problem with all of them is that they define laminitis as an inflammation or disease of the foot. As this book will show, it is actually an inflammatory disease of the whole horse with symptoms that erupt in many parts of the horse's body, including the feet. So long as horse owners and others treat it as a disease of the foot, the laminitis money trail will continue to grow and grow, measured in profits and equine misery. So, to be clear, laminitis is a symptom of what I understand to be a Whole Horse Inflammatory Disease (WHID). Accordingly, laminitis is the pathological separation of the hoof from the horse, a symptom of WHID. Because the term laminitis is so entrenched in the horse world today, I will continue to use it throughout this book, albeit with a reassigned meaning that it is a symptom of a whole body inflammatory disease. Some of this discussion will get a little technical, but not so much that a person with average intelligence can't understand it. It is important to understand what's going on though because escaping the clenches of the laminitis industry will require that you be sufficiently informed.

The conventional definition used most often by veterinarians, farriers and barefoot trimmers, and horse owners who've had to deal with it is *inflammation of the (dermal) lamina*, hence the term laminitis. *Lamina* actually refers to the network of dermal and epidermal leaf-like structures (*Figures 1-1* and *1-2*) that interlock together (called "interdigitation") to form a complex bridge of

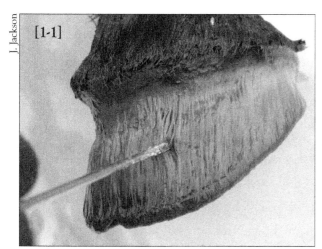
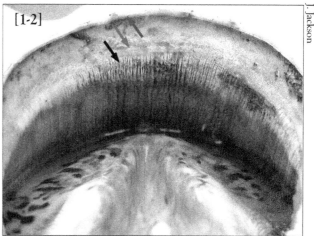

[1-1] Here, I am prying apart dermal leaves of a cadaver specimen with a probe. They are rich in blood and interdigitate with corresponding epidermal leaves (See *Fig. 1-2*). Behind the vast bed of dermal leaves is the lowermost bone of the hoof of the (See *Fig. 1-3*).

[1-2] The contents of the cadaver hoof have been emptied. Black arrow points to the epidermal leaves that lie between corresponding dermal leaves. Red arrow points to the inner hoof wall which surrounds and is contiguous with the epidermal leaves. Blue arrow points to the "crest" of the outer wall (see *Figure 1-3*) .

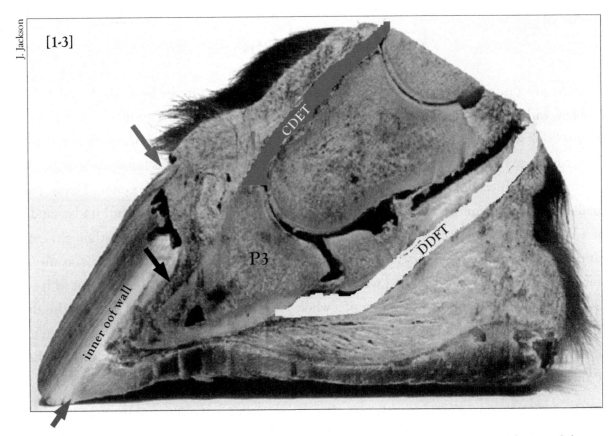

connective tissue between the inner hoof wall and the outer face of the lowermost bone of the horse's foot, called the coffin bone — known variously as the pedal bone, distal phalanx, and P3. Figure 1-3 shows the location of this bone in cross-section. This is an important image because the structures I've identified in it are typically clinically, and I believe, with great harm, implicated in the laminitic foot.

The black arrow points to the location of the interdigitated dermal and epidermal leaves, which are sandwiched everywhere between the inner hoof wall and P3. The blue arrow points to the *white line* at the bottom of the hoof, a familiar term to most horse owners. The red arrow points to the coronary band, behind which is seated the coronary dermis from which the hoof wall is produced and grows down past the dermal-epidermal leaves and P3. The blue zone corresponds to the Common Digital Extensor Tendon (CDET) which pulls the hoof forward. The yellow zone marks the Deep Digital Flexor Tendon (DDFT) which pulls the foot rearward. Both tendons are attached to P3 and the DDFT is a conventional target for surgical tenotomy (cutting) in the treatment of laminitis, which I do not recommend under any circumstances.

The body of a dermal leaf is comprised of fibrous connective tissue, and is both vascular (contains blood) and innervated (contains nerves). On one side, it is attached to the face of P3 through its connective tissue; on the other side, it interdigitates with the epidermal leaves. The epidermal leaves, in contrast, are also fibrous, but are neither enervated nor vascular. The two sets of leaves are connected together by what is called the Lamellar Attachment Mechanism, or "LAM", a term that we will revisit many times throughout this book. This "living bridge" between the leaves is structurally very complex but can be explained in sufficiently simple terms that we can understand what's happening to it in life when the horse is either sound or suffering from laminitis. Strategically, the LAM is very important because it enables the hoof wall to grow down past P3. How it does this is truly one of nature's wonders.

Looking closer at the dermal-epidermal interface reveals another layer of leaves between the two. At this point, we need to identify each of these leaf structures and explain what their roles are as part of the LAM. They can be seen in the electron micrograph in Figure 1-4. The epidermal structure marked PEL is the *primary epidermal leaf (laminae)*, which is born of its own dermal bed located at the lower shoulder of the inner hoof wall. As newly produced PELs emerge they are simultaneously cemented to newly produced inner hoof wall. At the same time, they are laced (interdigitated) between and attached to two dermal leaves, marked as DL in the micrograph. The DLs, firmly attached to P3 by means of their connective tissue, are stationary and do not grow downward. This presents a problem: how can the newly formed hoof wall (including the fused PELs) grow continuously downward and past the "fixed in place" dermal leaves if, at the same time, it has to remain attached (via the PELs)? Nature solves this in a truly amazing way!

Not seen in the micrograph, nor visible to the naked eye, is another component of each dermal leaf called the *basal* or *basement membrane*. This is a thin membranous layer of connective tissue that covers the underlying vascular tissue of the dermal leaf. Epithelial cells continuously proliferate from the basement membrane to form the *secondary epidermal leaves (lamina)*, or SEL. As each SEL is produced, it adheres to the "host" PEL through cellular migration and integration. At

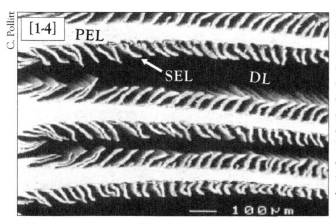

[1-4] **Nuclear magnetic resonated (NMR) image of structures comprising the LAM.** Don't fret over the scientific terminology and acronyms! The connective tissue of the dermal lamina (DL) anchors to P3 which is off to the right and out of view. The secondary epidermal lamina (SEL) are produced off the membranous surface of the dermal lamina, forming a bridge to the primary epidermal lamina (PEL) that form part of the inner hoof wall and enable the hoof wall to grow past P3 (See *Figure 1-5*).

PEL = primary epidermal lamina.
SEL = secondary epidermal lamina.
DL = dermal lamina.

[1-5] Simplification of the lamellar attachment mechanism (LAM) in action. This is a useful model for what's happening when the hoof wall descends past the dermal leaves (DL) and P3. Enzymes naturally present in the environment sever the dermal-epidermal bonds, enabling the hoof wall to grow continuously down past P3 (not shown in the diagram but would be on the right).

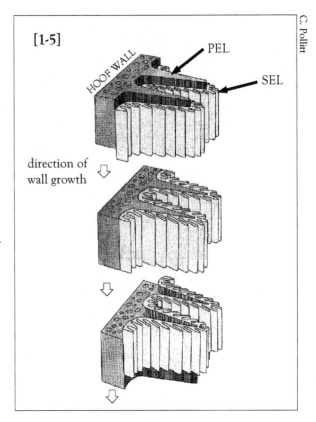

[1-5]

HOOF WALL

PEL

SEL

direction of wall growth

C. Pollitt

the same time — through the actions of specialized enzymes operative in the environment (called proteolysis) — its cellular bonds with the basement membrane are cleaved and replaced by new generations of proliferating epithelial cells. In this way, the hoof wall (including the attached PELs and integrated SELs) is detached and able to grow down past the stationary basement membrane and the underlying connective tissue of the dermal leaf, to which P3 is attached. The mechanisms involved are similar to the passage of your own finger/toe nails past their respective dermal beds. *Figure 1-5* is a simplification of these key players comprising a healthy and optimally functioning LAM. It is important to understand what happens to this vital bridge when laminitis strikes?

Pathophysiology

Laminitis is set off in the lower intestine by substances consumed (feeds, fluids, medications, supplements, etc.) or injected (medications such as antibiotics, sedatives, pain killers, steroids, vaccinations, etc.). All of these substances are not natural to the horse and they favor the colonization and proliferation of harmful bacteria to the detriment of those bacteria which are necessary and beneficial for healthy digestion and the uptake of vital nutrients.[1] All of these strains of bacteria and other microbes are naturally present in the horse's body at all times and their "harmonious" coexistence is an important cornerstone of the immune system's ecology. But during laminitis, harmful bacteria proliferate to the degree that beneficial microbes perish, creating an acidic and toxic environment that also erodes the gastric and intestinal mucosa (complex layers of biological membrane responsible for most digestive, absorptive, and secretory processes, including peristalsis). Bacteria (good and bad) and other intestinal debris are then pathologically absorbed into the blood stream and, overwhelming the body's natural immune system, travel to the

[1]*Streptococci bovis* and *S. equinus* have been identified by researchers as offending bacteria.

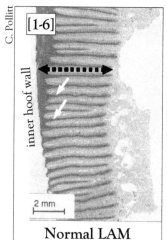

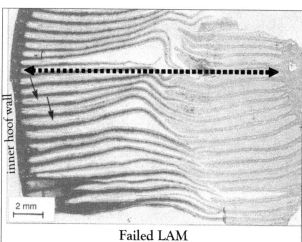

C. Pollitt

[1-6]

inner hoof wall

2 mm

Normal LAM

inner hoof wall

2 mm

Failed LAM

[1-6] Greatly magnified "normal" and "failed" LAM. P3 is out of view to the right of the large double arrows; inner hoof wall is on the left. White arrows point to the dark stained "primary epidermal leaves" (PEL) that connect the LAM to the inner hoof wall. Small black arrows point to the light stained dermal leaves that connect the LAM to P3. The failed LAM has widened by a magnitude of 5 x normal!

feet and elsewhere in the horse's body where they wreak havoc. In other words, I am talking about WHID, both its *pathophysiology* (functional changes that accompany the disease) and *pathogenesis* (origin or cause of the disease).

"Leaky gut syndrome" would be an example of this systemic degradation. This syndrome, however, basically defines the pathophysiology of Whole Horse Inflammatory Disease (WHID) and shouldn't be confused with its pathogenesis. The same syndrome in humans would have a parallel classification, "Whole Human Inflammatory Disease." But in either case (horse or human), the pathogenesis of WHID lies in what is being ingested. It is remarkable, to my way of thinking, that mainstream science is so rigidly myopic as to denigrate this syndrome as pseudoscience, although not all scientists are so sure and there is much ongoing research that is clearly pointing directly at WHID.[1] But so long as veterinarians and physicians in the field or office identify, isolate, and treat symptoms as diseases onto themselves, WHID will continue to manifest itself broadly and insidiously across both species with catastrophic implications for their patients. Laminitis is only one example in horses, and I will detail others later in this book.

At the foot, a particularly pernicious consequence of this contamination is its effect on those

[1]"Leaky gut syndrome". NHS Choices. 26 February 2015. Retrieved 15 August 2016.

Yarandi SS, Peterson DA, Treisman GJ, Moran TH, Pasricha PJ (2016). "Modulatory Effects of Gut Microbiota on the Central Nervous System: How Gut Could Play a Role in Neuropsychiatric Health and Diseases.". J Neurogastroenterol Motil (Review). 22 (2): 201–12. doi:10.5056/jnm15146. PMC 4819858free to read. PMID 27032544.

Akbari P, Braber S, Varasteh S, Alizadeh A, Garssen J, Fink-Gremmels J (2016). "The intestinal barrier as an emerging target in the toxicological assessment of mycotoxins". Arch Toxicol. doi:10.1007/s00204-016-1794-8. PMID 27417439.

Morris G, Berk M, Carvalho A, Caso JR, Sanz Y, Walder K, et al. (2016). "The Role of the Microbial Metabolites Including Tryptophan Catabolites and Short Chain Fatty Acids in the Pathophysiology of Immune-Inflammatory and Neuroimmune Disease". Mol Neurobiol (Review). doi:10.1007/s12035-016-0004-2. PMID 27349436.

Sung H, Kim SW, Hong M, Suk KT (2016). "Microbiota-based treatments in alcoholic liver disease.". World J Gastroenterol (Review). 22 (29): 6673–82. doi:10.3748/wjg.v22.i29.6673. PMC 4970471free to read. PMID 27547010.

Klingensmith NJ, Coopersmith CM (2016). "The Gut as the Motor of Multiple Organ Dysfunction in Critical Illness". Crit Care Clin (Review). 32 (2): 203–12. doi:10.1016/j.ccc.2015.11.004. PMC 4808565free to read. PMID 27016162.

[1-7 and 1-8] Arrows point to examples of failed LAM visible in the white line. Such disorganized lamellar epidermal mass is not always visible when sighting the bottom of the hoof, however. So insidious is the progression of laminitis that the white line may appear perfectly normal at ground level while extensive separation of the LAM occurs further up the dermal-epidermal lamellar scaffold.

enzymes discussed earlier that are naturally present in the LAM and are responsible for breaking down the epithelial cells of the basement membrane so that the hoof can naturally descend past P3. These enzymes now proliferate pathologically, destroying the dermal-epidermal cellular bonds that are responsible for securing the wall to P3 and faster than normal mechanisms involved can repair them. For this reason, I think of laminitis as a normal process gone awry. The LAM then begins to "stretch apart" as illustrated in *Figure 1-6*. If not halted by appropriate changes in the horse's diet, the LAM will continue to degrade and eventually become a tangled mass of disorganized growth. *Figures 1-7* and *1-8* are examples of hooves so affected.

This degradation of the LAM is accompanied by inflammatory symptoms within the foot, particularly during acute attacks; these may include severe pain, elevated temperatures, and a palpable pounding pulse above the coronary band. The severity of these symptoms, and the fact that such inflammation leads to deformity of the hoof itself, distract the horse owner from noticing symptoms occurring elsewhere across the horse's body. Or, if noticed, those symptoms are attributed to problems not related to laminitis at all. Indeed, if one studies the progression of the disease from the standpoint of the horse's entire body, then it becomes apparent that damage is not limited to the feet. Many years ago, I asked myself, if contamination is wreaking havoc to the horse's foot via the vascular system, then why wouldn't it affect all other parts of the body, including the internal organs and maybe even the brain? Looking at it this way is what has led me to redefine laminitis as a symptom of Whole Horse Inflammatory Disease (WHID).

Family band of wild, free-roaming horses living in central Nevada. Laminitis is unknown in the horse's natural world.

A natural consequence of viewing the disease as a whole body inflammatory degradation, is that I began to view its causality and treatment equally from a holistic "whole body" perspective. This meant trying to understand the vital biology of the species rather than focusing solely on pathology arguably caused by human mismanagement, and certainly not as a "disease of the foot." At first, this new line of thinking was highly speculative and based entirely on a presumption that nature surely would not have created a highly flawed species with terrible hooves after millions of years of evolutionary descent through natural selection. But with laminitis epidemic worldwide as far back as I can remember into the early 1970s, such as assumption was clearly not supported by the reality before me. In fact, any discussion to the contrary with others of my profession back then would have been met with ridicule, disdain, disbelief, or deigned irrelevance. It might have all ended right then had it not been for my adventures in wild horse country where I learned first hand that laminitis, like most equine diseases, does not exist in their natural world. It is entirely "man made".

I've been asked innumerable times since conducting and reporting my findings in wild horse country, what exactly is my purpose? The questions have flowed from many perspectives and disciplines dealing with horses that are living in domestication — ranging from the highest orders of altruistic concern and advocacy for the animal's well-being to simply, "Can it help me win competi-

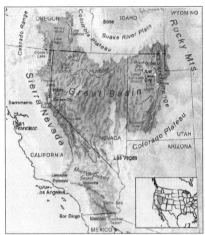

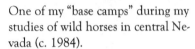
One of my "base camps" during my studies of wild horses in central Nevada (c. 1984).

tively?" Anticipating this diversity, I've tried to cover a lot of informational territory in my books, articles, clinics, and lectures. But if I were to distill my way through the variant interests and curiosity expressed to me, and answer the fundamental question of "purpose," it would be to raise and answer the question I posed to myself many years ago as I stood at the threshold of the U.S. Great Basin: through an understanding of the horse's natural world, what can I do for the horse, and not, what can the horse do for me. So, in the pages that follow, my purpose is not to heal the horse so that the horse can then serve me, but very simply, to do everything I can to restore his native vitality and to prevent this disease from ever happening again.

The good news is that when we apply the principles and proven practices of *natural horse care* ("NHC") based on my research of wild, free-roaming horses, healing and preventing laminitis is readily accomplished through basic and relatively simple changes in how we manage our horses. This is an entirely different approach than conventional veterinary and farriery therapeutic interventions that ignore causality and treat symptoms. Ignoring causality and nature's healing pathways, conventional care has resulted in treatment strategies that, in my opinion, are typically and unnecessarily mechanical, invasive, ineffective, and worse, damaging not only to the foot, but to the horse's overall well-being. Indeed, causality and prevention are marginalized and given little discussion, whereas misinformation is often propagated unwittingly by the farrier, veterinarian, and horse owner. NHC, once more, approaches laminitis holistically through making healthful changes in the horse's lifestyle that address causality, natural healing mechanisms, and prevention.

Chapter Two

What Causes Laminitis?

Laminitis, contrary to what many believe, does not origi-
nate in the horse's foot, but in the horse's digestive system.
Which is to say, it really begins with what the horse is eating
or what we've put into him such as pasture grass, sugary
feeds, and drugs — all of which upset the body's natural metabolic processes. I call these "laminitis triggers." Treating laminitis as though it originates or is limited to the foot is an invi-
tation to disaster. The reason that laminitis is so prevalent
and devastating in today's horse world, meaning countless
horses are debilitated by or die from it, is because it is treated
nearly in a vacuum as a foot disease. It isn't, and treatment
should never begin there regardless of how deformed the
hoof looks or the degree of pain the horse is suffering as a
result of the inflammation inside the hooves. I recognize that
such advice may be controversial, but I stand by it.

The foot's distress is but one of many symptoms of a
greater problem occurring throughout the horse's body. As I
wrote in the previous chapter, laminitis is actually a "whole
horse" disease because, symptomatically, it can adversely effect not only the feet, but almost any part of his body including the animal's sense of well-being. "Cresty necks," obesity,
psychological distress, hives, itchy skin, appearing to be ar-
thritic, and other types of lameness are all symptomatic of
laminitic horses. But at the bottom of it all is what has gotten
into his body and can't be processed without an assault on
the metabolic and immune systems.

Schematically, the flow chart (see *Table 2-1*) traces the
pathway of laminitis from trigger (cause) to a plethora of possible common symptoms that may surface sub-clinically
(absence of pain), clinically (presence of pain), and chroni-
cally (repeating sub-clinical and/or clinical symptoms over months or years). Specific triggers and
symptoms are taken up in greater detail in following chapters.

**Table 2-1
Laminitis Causal Pathway**

Any number of possible triggers.

↓

Harmful bacteria proliferate
in the lower intestine.

↓

Erosion of intestinal lining.

↓

Toxins are released into
the vascular system.

↓

Toxins migrate to
other parts of the body.

↓

Any number of *possible* symptoms
may erupt throughout the body.

↓

Sub-clinical symptoms
(no observable pain)

↓

Clinical symptoms
(observable pain)

↓

Chronic symptoms
(any reoccurring clinical
and/or sub-clinical symptoms)

Chapter Three
What are Laminitis "Triggers"?

Stated simply, laminitis triggers are any substances, natural or artificial, that distress the horse's metabolic processes resulting in laminitis. I distinguish those triggers that are naturally occurring from those that are "artificial." No one knows for sure what all the possible triggers are, moreover there is considerable disagreement between my own opinions and what conventional thinking is about the actual effects of any given trigger. For example, my experience has been that grass pastures and other vegetation that synthesize sugar are dangerous laminitis triggers (*Figure 3-1*). Horses will, in some degree, become laminitic if turned out long enough in the typical grass pastures used by horse owners.[1] Moreover, I am convinced that sugars in all forms are triggers, yet many horse feeds include significant amounts of molasses, sugar beet pulp, and/or cane sugar. My opinions are based on countless observations of horses in pasture turnouts and hundreds of laminitis consultations I have conducted over the years with horses fed regular diets of sweet feeds. Conventional science is less certain or — like the manufacturers of these products — ignores the issue altogether, and may even recommend putting horses in pasture turnouts supplemented with rich sweet feeds![2]

Artificial triggers are those biological, chemical, and agricultural products manufactured by the laminitis industry. They are probably the leading cause of laminitis because most horses are confined to small stalls and paddocks with little or no pasture turnout and these types of products are what's typically available — and encouraged by industry advertising — in today's feed stores. One can't walk into a feed store today and not smell the chemicals and sweet feeds that permeate the air. But whether triggers are natural, artificial, or synthesized together, they can be life-threatening if they aggressively overwhelm the horse's sensitive bacterial colonies.

Table 3-1 lists natural and artificial substances that I and others have either confirmed to cause laminitis, or are very suspect because they have been present along with known triggers in such a way that they cannot be ruled out with certainty. And, as notated in the table heading, triggers impact the digestive bacterial colonies according to a range of variables, including how much the horse has ingested, what the concentrations were, their frequency, and if more than one trigger was involved.

The picture, unfortunately, is further complicated by the fact that some horses are seemingly

---

[1] Grasses of the U.S. Great Basin high desert type seem safe based on my observations.

[2] This is beginning to change. Recent published research is supportive of the NHC position on grass chemistry relative to laminitis. See: "Weight Loss Management in Client-Owned Horses". Jennifer Christine Gill, Shannon Elizabeth Pratt-Phillips, Richard Mansmann, Paul David Siciliano. p80–89. *Journal of Equine Veterinary Science*. January 18 2016. See also; "Equine Laminitis: Managing Pasture to Reduce Laminitis." Dr. Christopher Pollitt and Katherine Watts, June 2010. Rural Industries Research and Development Corporation.

[3-1] Grass pastures are "laminitis traps" and are no place for any horse. But so are many standard commercial horse rations. Avoid any feed with free sugar or sugar waste products of any kind in it — cane, molasses, beet pulp, or fructan.

Table 3-1 Natural and Artificial Laminitis Triggers* (*Triggers may vary by quantity, concentration, and frequency.)			
Naturally occurring	**Artificial ("intentional human manufactured")**		
Vegetative	**Biological**	**Chemical**	**Agricultural**
Grasses, legume plants, and other vegetation that manufacture sugars.	• Vaccinations • Antibiotics • Steroids	• Fertilizers • Herbicides • Parasiticides • Pergolide • NSAIDS • Glyphosate • Propionic acid	All free sugars: cane, molasses, beet pulp, fructose, and artificial sweeteners.
			Feeds containing free sugars; corn, barley; waste products such as wheat middlings, mineral oil, rice bran, and formaldehyde; and anti-fungal chemicals such as propionic acid.

less sensitive to known triggers than are other horses. One horse may be very prone to acute attacks or chronic suffering, and another minimally so, even though both have ingested the same trigger within the same time frame. In short, while there are many possible laminitis triggers, not all horses may react the same to them. *At least in the short term.* And therein lies the principal problem and caveat: at what point does the digestive system's biological balances collapse — within hours resulting in an acute fatal attack, or slowly and insidiously over days and months with the hooves slowly unraveling as depicted in *Figures 1-7* and *1-8?* A major complication in all of this is that the many possible symptoms of laminitis may go unnoticed or be misinterpreted; for example, some chronic symptoms relating to compromised ambulation are often misdiagnosed as arthritis. Not that the horse might not also be suffering from arthritis, because both laminitis and arthritis are actually symptoms of WHID! For these reasons, horse owners are encouraged to consider these potential offending triggers closely and, if in doubt, err on the side of safety and take preventive measures to remove them from your horse's diet and veterinary care.

Regarding artificial triggers, I often ask myself, does the person in some far off laboratory, assembly line, warehouse, or hay field spraying glyphosate herbicide, have any idea of the problems their products are creating for horses? As one who is in the trenches of horse care dealing with their outfall into horses' lives, the laminitis industry is not just tinkering with the horse's immune system, they are playing a serious game of Russian Roulette with it. No one should be just dumping products into horses without truly understanding their impact in life. The profit motive is no justification, to my way of thinking, to look the other way. Understanding the horse's immune system and it's critical relationship to diet is of paramount importance in treating and preventing laminitis. The ethical thing to do would be for the laminitis industry to give this the focus and attention it deserves, put the brakes on churning out triggers in the global market that they have created, and reformulate their products based on good science that uses the wild horse model as their foundation.

Summary

In contrast to conventional therapies, I take (and teach) an entirely different and unique approach to laminitis treatment, particularly in the way we deal with its triggers. Basically it works like this: *known* triggers are removed entirely (or mostly so) from the horse's lifestyle, and the horse is then brought into the broad, holistic fold of NHC based on the wild horse model. This accomplishes a number of things: pain is mitigated; the inflammatory response of the triggers in the foot's dermal structures is calmed so that sensitive tissue (e.g., the LAM) can heal; and the body's vascular and digestive tracts are restored to their natural balance and vitality. Further, the same NHC intervention also serves to prevent laminitis, and, in the broader picture across the horse's entire body, WHID. This strategy is taken up in greater detail in Chapter 11. For now, let's continue our discussion of what constitutes laminitis and its various symptoms.

Chapter Four

What are the Symptoms of Laminitis?

Laminitis is an insidious disease, meaning the offending triggers must first overwhelm the immune system before an onslaught of symptoms begin to reveal themselves. Commonly, horse owners do not recognize the developmental symptoms of laminitis for what they actually are — if they take notice of them at all. This doesn't have to be the case at all. By the time you finish this book you'll be educated enough to identify the symptoms and know what corrective actions to take to halt the disease's progression. Even the most sudden acute attacks take time for the laminitis triggers to accumulate and take their toll. But whether early, acute or chronic, horse owners need to learn what the symptoms are and what to do when they are detected.

I divide laminitis pathophysiology into three stages of progressive development:

sub-clinical (absence of pain) → *clinical (observable pain)* → *chronic (sub-clinical + clinical)*

Note that this progression is the outcome of triggers introduced into the horse's body that I discussed in Chapter 2 and delineated in the "Laminitis Causal Pathway" seen in *Figure 2-1*. It is this pathway precisely that is so important to understand because once the symptoms begin to erupt, the disease's "footprint" is established. Prevention is the first tier of defense against laminitis and this means eliminating the triggers before they precipitate the onset of symptoms. The second tier of defense is knowing the disease's sub-clinical symptoms because damage to the LAM can still be prevented in many cases or kept to a minimum. One laminitis progresses to the clinical (acute) stage, however, it is too late — the damage is done, not just to the hoof but possibly to other parts of the horse's body too. Worse yet, if the symptoms are allowed to progress into the chronic stage, we are looking at the likelihood of extreme hoof deformity, damage to body organs, gait obstruction, personality disorders, and the possibility of death due to shock from metabolic toxicity. The supplier of "hoof cadavers" for my training clinics relates there are many deaths per day due to laminitis on his pickup route (*Figure 4-1*). And he is only one of many licensed companies operating in the Southern California region. Of the hundreds of cadavers that reach my clinics each year, less than a few percent show no symptoms of laminitis; upwards of 75 percent of the remaining show chronic symptoms. Some are of such mind-boggling deformity that one wonders why there was no law enforcement involved. But close examination is revealing that the hoof care providers simply did not know what to do and that the line between abusive neglect and simple ignorance was too murky to bring charges against anyone. I've decided to share a small sampling of these specimens — both barefoot and shod — later in this chapter so that readers understand the depth and extent to which horses suffer in the world today from this disease.

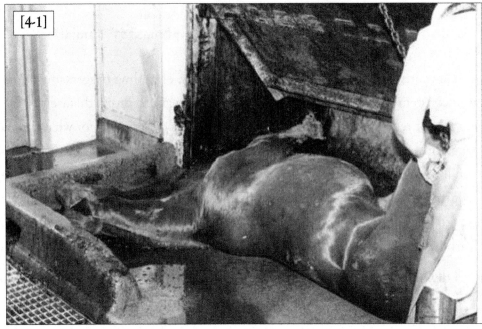

[4-1] With much ambivalence I decided to include this disturbing image of yet another casualty of the laminitis epidemic. Such scenes are hidden away in the shadows of the horse world, and the public for that matter. Arguably, the laminitis industry has unwittingly crafted the greatest equine holocaust in history in the name of profits.

Before identifying the symptoms of laminitis as it progresses through each of its three stages, it is important to understand also that not all symptoms may occur in each stage. Further, some symptoms may occur in all three stages and that in the chronic stage, many symptoms may come and go. *Table 4-1* outlines the general progression of the disease, stage by stage, including those symptoms likely to occur at each stage. Discussion of these symptoms with images follow in their progressive order in the remaining pages of this chapter.

Sub-clinical stage

First to arrive are the symptoms of the *sub-clinical stage* wherein there is no observable pain. Hence, the impact of the offending trigger (or triggers) is mild — insufficient, in other words, to precipitate clinical symptoms. These symptoms may include a subtle widening of the white line (see *Figure 4-2*), which is the result of early failure of the LAM (see *Figure 1-6*); reddish discoloration within the "white line[1]" due to blood seeping from an inflamed LAM (*Figure 4-3*); and/or emergence of stress rings in the outer wall (*Figure 4-4*). These three symptoms can be so subtle that

(Continued on page 27)

---

[1]"White line" is a misnomer because there is nothing white about it at all. Its scientific name is *Stratum lamellatum*. It is the epidermal bridge between the sole and inner hoof wall, visible at the bottom of any hoof. It is more the color of rawhide, as you can see in your own horse's hooves or in many of the photos in this book. The white band of color you can see outside the *S. lamellatum* in a freshly trimmed hoof is actually part of the inner hoof wall and is generically known as the "water line." Yet another misnomer, it is arguably the driest and hardest part of the naturally shaped hoof wall. Technically called the *Stratum internum*, it is the most salient structure of the "mustang roll" and is given much critical attention in the final steps of the natural trim. See my book, *The Natural Trim: Principles and Practice* (2012).

Table 4-1
Three Stages of Laminitis
and Their Symptoms

Any number of
possible triggers.

↓

Sub-clinical Stage

↙   ↓   ↘

Widening of white line	Stress rings in outer wall	Blood in white line

↓

Clinical (Acute) Stage

Any Sub-clinical or Clinical Symptoms, plus any of the following:

↙   ↓   ↘

Foot pain	Tendency to stand and lie down repeatedly	Heavy breathing
Founder stance	Constant left-right, right-left shifting of body weight	Sweating
Pounding pulse (foot)	Shock-Death	Anxiety

↓

Chronic Stage

Any Sub-clinical or Clinical Symptoms, plus any of the following:

↙   ↓   ↘

Cresty neck	Hoof slough	Off-on lameness
Severe hoof deformity	Unnatural hair growth/loss	P3-penetration
Lamellar wedge	P3-rotation	Hoof slough
Dropped sole	Thrush	Colic

[4-2] **Widening of the white line** (*Stratum lamellatum*). Black arrows point to subtle separation of the sole from the toe wall, blue arrow points to a significant separation and gap. Both occurrences are caused by a deterioration of the LAM in the dermis within the hoof. These pathological changes are also typical of the chronic stage of laminitis but are typically much more severe. Horse owners should keep a vigilant watch of the this stratum in their horse's hooves. This is not possible, of course, if the horse is shod, necessitating an evaluation between shoeings.

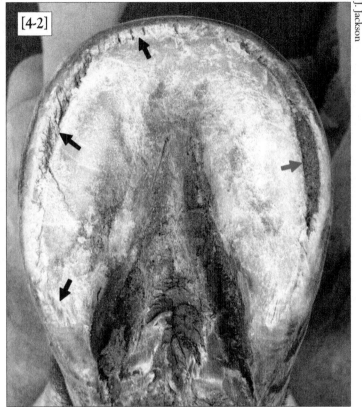

[4-3] **Blood in the white line** (*Stratum lamellatum*). Arrow points to section of white line in a living hoof that was permeated with red (blood) — the result of an inflamed, "leaky" LAM. NHC turned this horse around and he now wears natural shaped hooves, free of laminitis. Look for "spotting" or segments with blood as it is rare for the entire white line to be perfused. This is another symptom horse owners can be on the look out for. However, it often must be conducted during the trim session when the outer, dry layers of the white line have been freshly removed, thereby exposing the moist tissue within harboring blood.

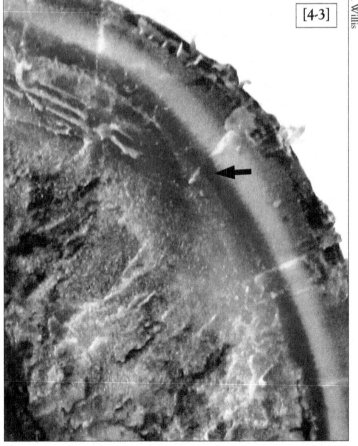

[4-4]

J. Jackson

[4-4] Stress rings in the outer wall. This is one of the more readily observable symptoms that erupt during the sub-clinical stage, but are prominent at later stages, too. Black arrow points to recent ring emerging below the coronary band during this stage. When this happens, horse owners should be concerned that an acute laminitic attack may be imminent and take preventive measures (Chapter 11). Blue arrows point to older lower rings, suggesting strongly that this hoof has been chronically laminitic.

(Continued from page 24)

they are typically unnoticed by an unsuspecting horse owner. They may also go unnoticed by the farrier or vet, or if noticed, are attributed to changes in the weather or feed, or other explanations that have no causal relationship to the inflammatory changes that are occurring in the LAM.

It goes without saying that of all the symptoms associated with laminitis, those associated with the sub-clinical stage are the most important ones horse owners should be familiar with. The reason is that they are clear indicators that the horse has become laminitic, but that there may still be time to prevent or mitigate the onset of devastating clinical symptoms.

Clinical (or "acute") stage

Next to arrive are the symptoms of the *clinical stage*, characterized by observable pain, obstruction of the natural gaits, and other overt changes in the horse's body, demeanor and metabolic processes. Clinical stage symptoms are listed in *Table 4-1. The clinical stage is defined as a medical emergency.* The horse may alternately get up and lay down frequently in an effort to mitigate pain in his feet. While standing, he may assume the "founder stance" extending his front legs out in front of him while holding his hind feet further under his torso than is normal in an effort to unload weight from his aching front feet (*Figure 4-5*). While there may not be extreme hoof deformation yet, there are usually other clear symptoms of foot distress present, including palpably abnormal heat emanating from the hoof, a bounding digital pulse above the cartilages, blood now saturating the while line, and stress rings emerging in the hoof's outer wall.

Horses that survive the clinical phase, but are not afforded NHC holistic care, or even consistent NHC care, typically begin to exhibit *chronic stage symptoms* if the triggers aren't entirely removed.

[4-5] **Horse in "founder stance."** The front hooves are severely deformed, indicating that the disease has also progressed to the chronic state.

[4-5]

A. Thayne

Chronic stage

Symptoms of the *chronic stage* tend to be off and on, and may include any of the previous symptoms (sub-clinical and clinical) plus a range of possible hoof deformities, aberrant upper body hair growth, dysfunctional internal organs, inability to move naturally, and neurotic psychological distress. Horses living with chronic symptoms are very miserable and unhappy animals. Unfortunately, the very forgiving and tractable nature of most horses encourages many owners to accept chronic symptoms and expect the horse to live with them too. Other horses in chronic pain and under the pressure of unreasonable human demands, however, may dissociate and become psychotic — dangerous to be around. Typically, their owners will solicit their vets to prescribe pain and "behavior control" medications and/or farriers to deploy the latest farrier technology to reconstruct the hooves to make them appear less deformed and temporarily palliate lameness. Others simply put their horses down due to perceived untreatability, or because they can't afford extended care, or they don't think the horse is worth the time or money for uncertain or lengthy rehabilitation. We often hear, "I can't keep him around if I can't ride him." In any case, these are all bleak outcomes for the chronically laminitic horse.

The most severe hoof deformity seen in the chronic stage is the "slipper toe" and its variations. It is defined by the toe wall, which is either "bent" (*Figure 4-9*), "curved" (*Figure 4-10*), "straight" (*Figure 4-11*), or "wry" (*Figure 4-12*), and is growing at an angle that is unnaturally low.

R. Zhu

[4-6] **"Cresty neck"**. This is a unnatural thickening of the upper neck. Conventionally it is that to be a cause or precursor to laminitis; in fact, it is one of many symptoms of chronic laminitis occurring elsewhere than the foot.

When the heels of such hooves are not shortened sufficiently according to natural trim guidelines, they are also said to be "run under" because the natural position of the bottom of the hoof is displaced too far forward for optimal support due to the excess heel growth.

In the remaining pages of this chapter are various images of laminitic hooves which have reached the chronic stage. It is important to realize, however, that horses in all three stages can be rehabilitated to soundness using the proven principles and practices of genuine NHC based on the wild horse model. Table 4-2 lists the most common symptoms seen in the chronic stage of laminitis, with page references to images and further discussion.

[Table 4-2] Chronic Stage Symptoms		
Figure	Page	Symptom
4-6	29	"Cresty neck"
4-7	30	Extreme white line separation
4-8	30	Thrush
4-9	31	Slipper toe ("bent")
4-10	31	Slipper toe ("straight")
4-11a,b	32	Slipper toe ("curved")
4-12a,b,c	33	Slipper toe ("wry")
4-13	36	Lamellar wedge ("ground level")
4-14	37	Lamellar wedge ("internal")
4-15	38	Hoof slough
4-16	39	Quarter crack

[4-7] **Extreme white line separation.** This is caused by extensive LAM failure resulting in broad degradation of the white line and separation of hoof wall from sole. This condition is also known as "White Line Disease" — a mischaracterization and misnomer of the actual pathology (chronic laminitis).

[4-8] **Thrush** is another misnomer disguising the actual problem, that is, it is a symptom of "laminitis" erupting in the frog. But, here again, the laminitis money trail has rendered it into another profitable way to treat symptoms rather than cause. Who doesn't have thrush medications in the tack room's medicine cabinet? Many myths plague the frog, such as the "frog pressure theory", wherein the frog is thought to be a "pressure pump" vital to circulation but for which there is no shred of evidence. Another problem diametrically opposed to the pump theory is that the frog must be trimmed of all its "loose flaps" to prevent thrush.

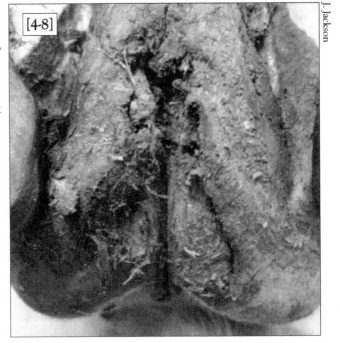

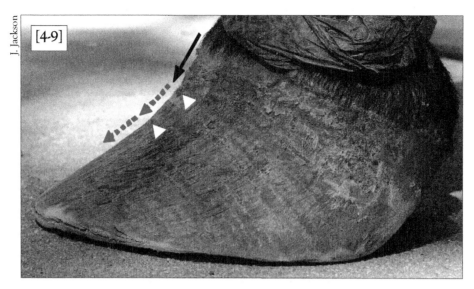

[4-9] **Slipper toe ("bent").** *Blue arrows* parallel the bent segments of the lower toe wall; *black arrow* parallels the newly forming toe wall (called the "Healing Angle" in NHC science[1]); *white triangles* point to the intersections of the wall segments. Typically, the slipper toe forms concurrently with lamellar wedge formation (*Figures 1-8* and *4-14*), but not always as the most severe slipper toe may form without any such disorganized epidermal mass. Slipper toes can be restored to the toe wall's natural angle, but this requires impeccable adherence to advanced natural trim guidelines and the owner's diligent allegiance to the 4 Pillars of NHC (*Chapter 11*).

[1]See in *Resources*: J. Jackson, *The Healing Angle: Nature's Gateway to the Healing Field* (2012). Also: J. Jackson, *The Natural Trim – Principles & Practice.*

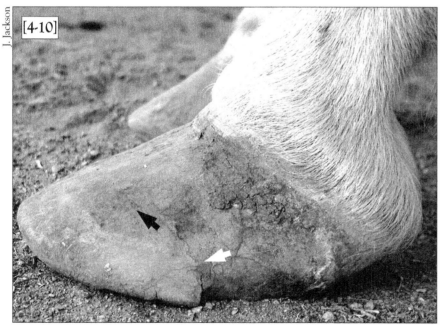

[4-10] **Slipper toe ("straight").** This chronically laminitic hoof is severely run-under, and while not "bent" or "curved", it meets the slipper toe test because it is growing at an angle that is unnaturally low. Although "run under", the heels are actually much too long. *White arrow* points to split in hoof wall, cleaving along a stress ring (*black arrow*). I was unable to convince the owner to roll back the horse's "laminitis diet" to a reasonably natural one, so it was impossible to help this horse. My ethical code prevents me from facilitating harmful managements through complicity, so I terminated my services.

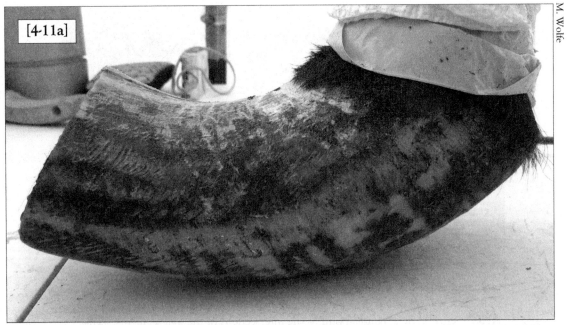

[4-11a,b] **Slipper toe ("curved")**. The "curved" slipper toe seen here (*Figure 4-11a*) is a common variation of the "straight" slipper toe conformation seen in *Figure 4-9*. The heels of this type of slipper toe commonly share the same arced conformation (*Figure 4-11b*). Arguably, the curved slipper toe is a man-made "run away" manifestation of the straight type, the trimmer being unable to stop the aberrant growth pattern. While NHC advanced natural trim guidelines determine to the millimeter where the toe and heels are to be shortened to without causing harm and facilitating future healthy growth patterns, traditional farrier and generic barefoot trimmers are less certain and even less specific, typically resecting the toe wall altogether or cutting off the end with a hack saw as was done here. Both "methods" are considered inhumane by NHC standards for humane hoof care.

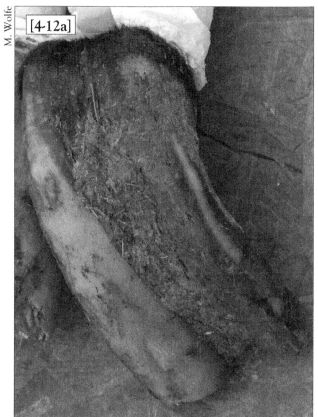

[4-12a]

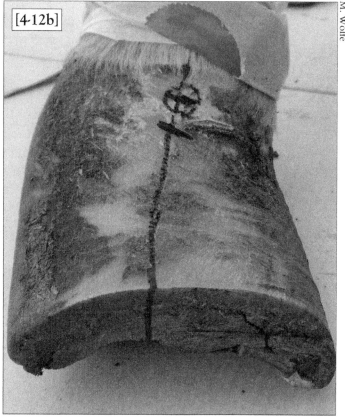

[4-12b]

M. Wolfe

M. Wolfe

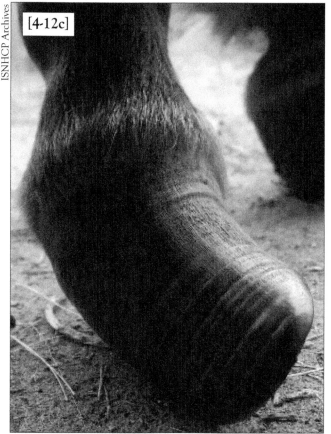

[4-12c]

ISNHCP Archives

[4-12a,b,c] Slipper toe ("wry"). Slippered toes that are wry — meaning growing and twisting in a direction that is unnatural — represent some of the worst case scenarios possible in aberrant hoof growth patterns. The only good news here is that they can be reined in by the natural trim over time. Figures 4-12*a* and 4-12*b* above are of the same hoof, one of the worst cadaver cases to arrive in one of my training clinics. The hoof in Figure 4-12*c* isn't any better off as the horse is unable to support himself on the bottom of his hoof at all. In both cases, these slipper toed chronically laminitic hooves are simultaneously bent, curved, wry, and the heels are run under.

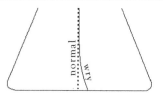

In the wry hoof viewed from the front, the epidermal "grain" of the toe wall grows down in a curve to the left or right instead of straight down as it does in a naturally shaped hoof. This can occur very subtlety or with great exaggeration as seen in *Figure 4-12c.*

33

[4-13] Lamellar wedge ("ground level"). *White arrow* points to the edge of the sole, which has separated completely from the hoof wall. *Black arrow* points to lamellar wedge in the wake of white line separation. The horse's owner, a rancher, worked with me on getting his horse out of the pasture and moved to a safe diet with oats and hay. But after several trim sessions, the hooves continued to deteriorate. Baffled, we did a bit of detective work, only to discover that his wife was "feeling sorry" for the horse, believing that he must be "hungry" without access to the pasture, and, acting in secrecy, began to feed him a carbohydrate diet rich in molasses, corn, and other laminitis triggers!

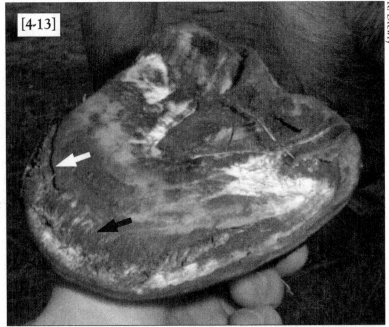

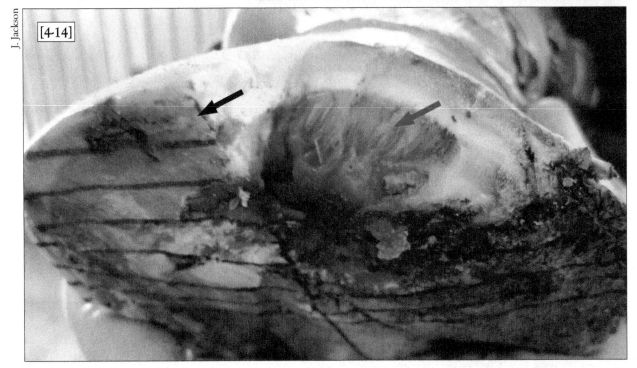

[4-14] Lamellar wedge ("internal"). Cadaver hoof following a dissection during one of my ISNHCP training clinics. *Blue arrow* points to LAM that has degraded into a moist "pocketed" lamellar wedge (LW) half way up the inner hoof wall. It is not widely recognized by hoof care practitioners that LW can occur anywhere along the LAM, as in this case where it is has occurred internally and not at ground level where the white line is only marginally separated (*black arrow*). LW can also vary in mass (L x W x H) as well as in moisture content; for example, it will be desiccated and insensitive anywhere from the dermal junction of the sole with the inner hoof wall down to ground level where we recognize it as "stretched white line" (e.g., *Figure 1-8*), but very moist and sensitive anywhere above that due to the presence of active vascular and enervated dermal lamina in the LAM. Eventually, all LW is expelled through the white line corridor by new replacement growth descending from above. [Photo: J. Jackson]

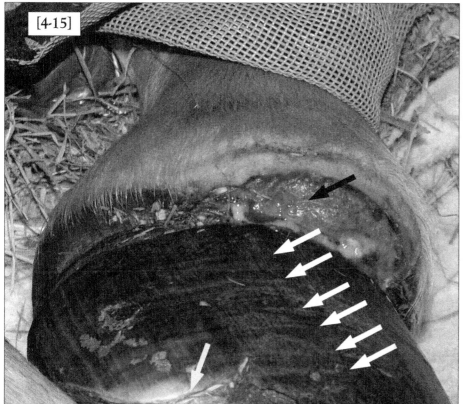

[4-15] **Hoof Slough.** This hoof is literally oozing off due to catastrophic failure of the LAM, possibly complicated by secondary infection or excessive antibacterial medicating since NHC targets antibiotics as potential laminitis triggers. *Black arrow* points to herniating coronary corium, the dermal structure responsible for creating and maintaining the hoof wall. *White arrows* point to a steady stream of cascading stress rings. *Yellow arrow* points to a thin veneer of ragged outer wall near its ground bearing surface. Short of death, hoof slough is the worst case scenario of laminitis chronicity. Horses can survive this to grow an entirely new hoof, but even with exemplary NHC intervention, the healing pathway isn't easy for the horse. [Photo: ISNHCP Archives]

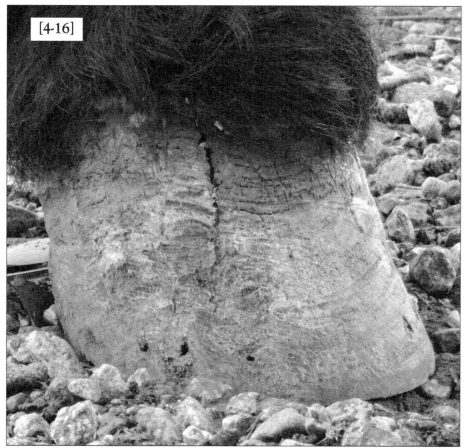

[4-16] **Quarter crack.** Quarter cracks occur from the coronary band down and are distinguished from wall splits which open from the ground up. Quarter cracks are common in chronic cases because of the relative instability of the hoof wall due to diet, drugs, unnatural hoof care methods, and the fact that the wall is naturally thinner near its crest (*Figures 1-2* and *1-3*). This horse was subject to all four. High doses of steroids rendered the wall into a rubber like consistency, if not the worst case of epidermal tissue degradation I had seen in 45 years, certainly the most bizarre. We'll revisit this hoof in *Chapter 7* (*Figure 7-1*). [Photo: L. Tanner]

Chapter Five

What is "Founder"?

Founder, technically, is a consequence of laminitis. The term is often used synonymously with laminitis, but there is a difference. Specifically, founder means that the lowermost bone of the horse's foot has separated from the hoof wall due to a catastrophic failure of the LAM (Chapter 1). While separation may commence as early as the sub-clinical stage of laminitis, it is more associated with the chronic stage when it is conventionally confirmed through radiography. Commonly, founder is also known as *P3-rotation*, although other bones of the digit may also rotate (e. g., P2/P3-rotation), depending on the severity of the damage to the LAM. Arguably, "digital rota-

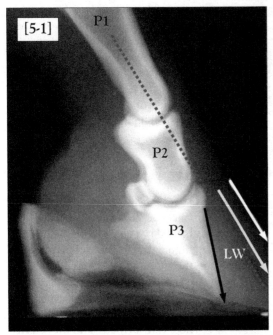

[5-1] **Radiographic evidence of "P3-rotation".** *Black arrow* traces the dorsal axis (front angle or slope) of P3. *White arrow* traces the slope of the outer toe wall. *Yellow arrow* traces the slope of the inner hoof wall where it normally adjoins P3. The broken *blue line* marks the "digital axis", equivalent to the familiar "slope of the pastern", wherein the bones of the digit (P1-P2-P3) are said to be aligned with the toe wall (*white arrow*). During P3-rotation, the digital axis is broken and the bones do not align, which is the case here since P2 and P3 have rotated behind the axis, hence this is an example of P2P3-rotation rather than "P3-rotation". The angle formed between the black arrow and digital axis (*broken blue line*) relative to flat ground can be measured in degrees and is equal to the "angle of rotation". The space between the black and yellow arrows is filled with lamellar wedge (LW). [Photo: ISNHCP archives]

tion" is a more accurate term. *Figures 5-1* and *5-2* are examples of digital rotation.

It has been thought — conventionally so — that the front tip of P3 plunges (i.e., rotates) towards the sole due to weight bearing forces pressing down upon it as a consequence of the LAM's failure. In this interpretation, P3-rotation is measured radiographically by degrees of change from its "normal" position relative to the "digital axis" of P1-P2-P3 from the outer hoof wall (e.g., 10 degrees of rotation). In contrast, NHC science holds that there is no weight borne at all by P3 and that there is another explanation. Specifically, any such purported "rotation" is attributed to the presence of lamellar wedge (LW) and normal interphalangeal joint flexion between the bones of the digit relative to the hoof wall. As the LW proliferates in mass due to the failed LAM, the hoof wall forms a slipper toe while P3 slowly moves towards the ground (hence, the "rotation"). The *rate of rotation* is governed by the rate of the LW proliferation; the *degrees of rotation* possible is determined by the overall mass of LW present and the limits of interphalangeal joint flexion that govern how far P3 can rotate down. Of course, the driving force behind all of these pathological changes are the laminitis triggers.

Another possible consequence of founder is what is called "P3-penetration", wherein the sharp tip of P3 literally pierces the sole (*Figure 5-3*). Conventional thought holds that

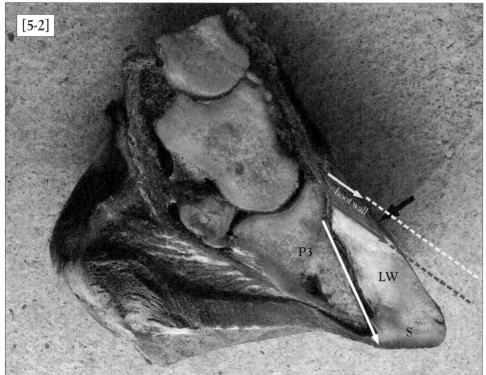

[5-2] Cross-section of cadaver (not the same hoof in *Figure 5-1*) showing extent of P3 rotation. *White arrow* traces the dorsal axis (front angle or slope) of P3. *Yellow arrow* traces the slope of the outer toe wall. *Blue arrow* traces the slope of the inner hoof wall where it normally adjoins P3. *Black arrow* points to the end of the hoof wall, which has been cut off. *Yellow and blue dashed lines* mark the direction and approximate length of the toe wall had it not been resected. *LW* marks the lamellar wedge. *S* marks the sole. By the way, this hoof was trimmed in violation of NHC guidelines for the natural trim — the toe wall is shortened to within a inch of the coronary band, rather then left to approximate it's natural length. [Photo: A. Brollo]

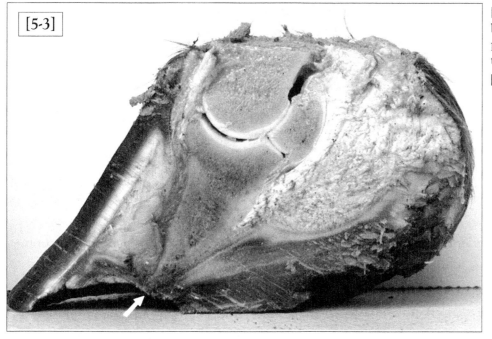

[5-3] Cross-section of a cadaver biospecimen. White arrow points to tip of P3 protruding through the "dropped sole. [Photo: J. Jackson]

the penetration is due to weight bearing forces driving P3 downward into and through the sole. NHC science says otherwise, that what is happening is the extrusion of "corrupted" epidermal sole produced by a sick solar corium. This is no different than the production of lamellar wedge between P3 and the hoof wall. Called a "dropped sole" by convention, the term is actually a misnomer because nothing is actually "dropping" in the same sense that nothing is actually

[5-4] "Dropped Sole". Arrow points to an enormous mound of protective solar mass below the distal periphery of P3, also common with chronic cases suffering with dropped soles. [Photo: J. Jackson]

"rotating" either. Hence, the "penetration" is simply due to corrupted epidermis collapsing around the sharp distal edge of the bone at whatever P3's "angle of rotation" (due to lamellar wedge) might happen to be. This penetration is short-lived, however, if the offending laminitis triggers are eliminated. The solar corium will begin to build an enormous convex "mound" of protective, hard, epidermal callous around the penetrating edge of P3 (*Figure 5-4*). A healing mechanism, the mass is left intact during the natural trim until such time that it exfoliates gradually on its own (like bark shed by a tree) to restore its unique concaved architecture under the full force of NHC holistic practices.

In summary, founder encompasses — in addition to the other symptoms of laminitis chronicity — the possible egregious pathological outcomes of P3-rotation and P3-penetration. Further, according to NHC science, founder is not really about "rotating bones" causing havoc under weight bearing forces; indeed, it is entirely about aberrant growth patterns and the proliferation of a lamellar wedge due to laminitis triggers caused by unnatural care. Not to despair, the good news is that by shutting down those triggers, the sole will stop "dropping" and P3 will cease "rotating" — or, depending on the progression of the disease, neither will happen significantly at all — and healing can commence. Our next objective, whatever the degree of the disease's progression, will be to reconstruct a healthy bond between the hoof wall, the underlying dermis, and P3 via a rehabilitated LAM. Happily, founder, like laminitis in all its stages, is entirely preventable and healable through NHC holistic practices. This will include, in the most deformed hooves, using the Advanced Natural Trim Guidelines; these should only be conducted by an AANHCP practitioner trained in their specialized use and protocols.

Chapter Six

"What do I do when there is an acute attack of laminitis?"

Acute laminitis is characterized by clinical symptoms (*Figure 4-1*). All horses so afflicted will assume the "founder stance" (*Figure 4-5*) and, finding no relief, alternately sand up and lay down on the ground repeatedly. Acute laminitis is considered a medical emergency and horses are at risk of death from shock due to metabolic toxicity and painful inflammation.

My first recommendation for action is to consult immediately with an AANHCP practitioner if possible (see *Resources*) and a vet for pain management if warranted. The AANHCP practitioner should be qualified to guide you — or willing to consult with someone who is qualified in the organization — and your horse through what will typically be a very winding pathway out of a very complicated and potentially dangerous situation. My opinion is that, because of the many factors associated with causality (*Chapter 2*), it can be a challenge for horse owners wanting to go it alone. Without some training in the science and holistic practices of NHC, horse owners will inevitably panic and pursue conventional treatment pathways, or get lost in the penumbra of bogus "holistic" and "natural" alternatives that may be equally harmful. I do advise strongly against conventional veterinary and farriery interventions (*Chapter 7*), with the following possible exceptions — and always after consulting your AANHCP practitioner first: the vet should confirm a diagnosis of laminitis and, at your practitioner's or consultant's discretion, prescribe pain medication. If your horse is shod, your AANHCP practitioner or consultant will advise when it is appropriate to remove the shoes, and will either do this themselves or have you bring the "shoer" back to do it. Shoes are typically removed once the horse is clearly capable of standing without pain on his own in order to give his feet freely — usually when severe pain has abated and the founder stance is no longer assumed.

> Practically speaking, you will need to take action whether or not an AANHCP practitioner is available in your area. Assuming this is the case, and after reading all the chapters in this book, go to Chapter 12 and diligently follow the NHC coordinated action plan for laminitis recovery.

"My horse has been chronically laminitic, what do I do now?"

The approach to recovery for chronically laminitic horses is, strategically speaking, the same as treating an acute attack, but, tactically, may require a broader range of NHC interventions. This is because it is common for chronic cases to involve a range of triggers that have affected the horse repeatedly over extended periods of time, as well as a plethora of harmful conventional veterinary and farrier "therapies" that have created damage in their own right – arguably worse than the disease itself! Accumulatively, these take a greater toll on the horse and his hooves than the other stages of laminitis. *Chapter 14* lays out the NHC action plan for healing chronic cases with severely deformed hooves. In the following pages are examples of increasingly common hoof care methods and their pernicious effects to be avoided at all costs in the meantime. These are summarized in Table 7-1.

Table 7-1 Common Hoof Care Procedures to Avoid for Treating Chronic Laminitis		
Figure	Page	Therapy
7-1	46	*Thinned sole*
7-2	46	*Pads*
7-3a,b	47	*Egg bar shoe*
7-4	48	*4 Point Trim*
7-5	48	*Heart bar shoe*
7-6	49	*Clog*
7-7	49	*Grooving*
7-8a,b	50	*Wall resection*
7-9	51	*White line strategy trim*
7-10	51	*Tube trim*
7-11a-e	52-53	*Clamping devices*

[7-1] *Thinned sole.* I discussed another view of this hoof in (*Figure 4-16*), but this one is probably more useful to us here because it illustrates the consequences of shoeing and also the rationale for yet several other methods (*Figures 7-2 and 7-3*) for dealing with dropped sole (*Figure 5-3 and 5-4*, and nearby *Chapter 5* text). What is happening here is a dropped sole that has been carved and rasped until it is flat as a pancake and virtually all solar concavity removed. This imperils the foot even more by removing crucial epidermal armor necessary for protecting the sensitive structures within. "Sole thinning" also makes it even harder for the horse to move because it renders the already inflamed dermis even more hypersensitive. [Photo: L. Tanner]

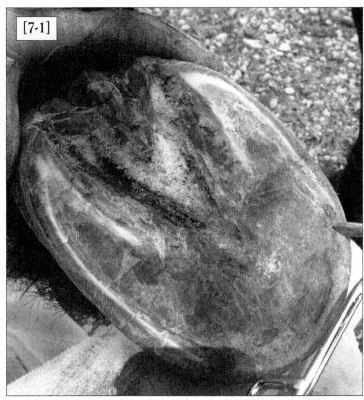

[7-2] *Pads.* Pads are yet another way to "mask" problems while blocking natural transpiration of moisture out the bottom of the foot. I removed these from the hoof above. The horse's sole is designed by nature to "breathe" like our own skin and nails, and communicate growth pattern information to its nerve bed from ground contact. So padding only serves to soften the hoof, weaken or harm its internal support structures (convex sole and vascular system) that are already distressed, trap pathogens within that will thrive in that type of environment and will act to exacerbate thrush, and cut off important communication networks. Packing agents put under the pad to control disease typically contain harmful chemicals that can be absorbed into the foot and will transport through the vascular system wreaking havoc in their own right. The sole needs to be exposed to the environment to heal and harden off through natural wear. [Photo: L. Tanner]

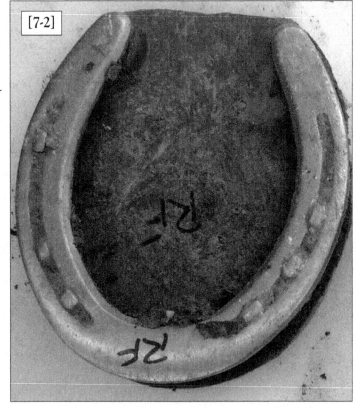

[7-3a]

[7-3a,b] *Egg bar shoe.* The egg is the eponymous inspiration for this shoe, whose purported premise is to provide extra "support" for the caudal (rear) extremities of the hoof. But the rationale is bogus because nature has amply provided for all the necessary support with the frogs, heel-buttresses, and allied internal structures, all of which are now rendered dysfunctional. Moreover, a laminitic foot already in pain is only compromised more by the presence of this steel trap, which further precludes ground contact thereby causing foot contraction and the incapacitation of the hoof's natural flexions that are strategic to optimal circulation, concussion mitigation, and support itself. As with all horseshoes, remove these from your horse to facilitate natural healing. Black arrow (*Figure 7-3b*) points to herniating coronary corium — the hoof is getting ready to slough. [Photos: J. Jackson]

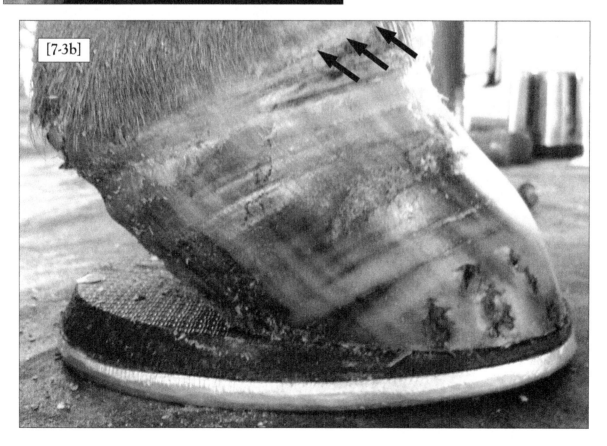

[7-3b]

[7-4] *4 Point Trim.* This shoe is flat across the toe and is commonly chamfered along with the entire toe wall and sole before being nailed on. White broken line marks the axis along which the toe wall and sole are beveled forward and rendered passive ("off the ground"), leaving 4 active wear points (yellow dots) to support the hoof. In fact, this shoe was designed to fit the "4 Pt. Trim", purported to mimic the natural wear patterns of the wild horse hoof, which it does not do. *Avoid at all costs.* [Photo: J. Jackson]

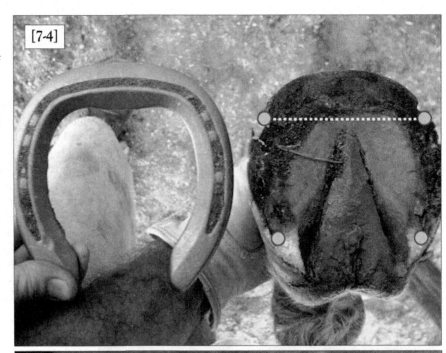

[7-5] *Heart bar shoe.* The heart bar shoe has probably been around for over a century, but was resurrected from the past by the late farrier Burney Chapman during the early 1980s. Eponymously named for the medieval ideographic heart seen today on playing cards and Cupid's "wounded heart" symbol , the principal idea behind the shoe is to provide support for P3 passively through the frog. *Black arrow* points to frog; *white arrow* to the salient "dented" base of the heart. Like the egg bar shoe, it is also alleged to provide broad, volar, and therapeutic support for hooves in distress. However, we recall according to NHC science, that P3 does not transport weight to the capsule, rather it is "weightless" and possesses no such force either to precipitate P3-rotation or P3-penetration (*Chapter 5*). Hence, the rationale for the heart bar shoe, like the egg bar shoe, is without merit, and both should be *avoided at all costs.* [Photo: G. Moon]

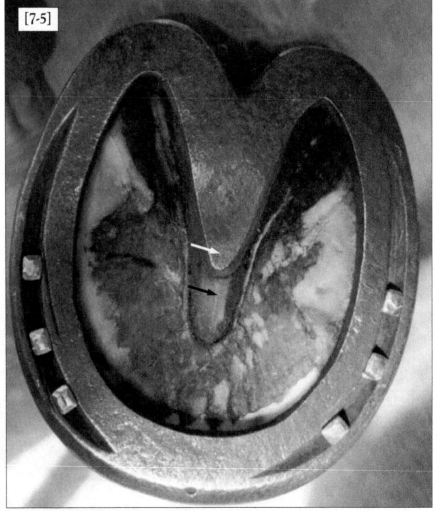

[7-6] *Clog.* (*Right*) This is a wooden shoe in the shape of a bowl, a variation of the "Steward Clog", the brain child of Oklahoma veterinarian Michael Steward. As can be seen the toe wall was resected to fit this monstrosity, and screws deployed to keep it attached to the hoof! The concept behind it is that the bowl facilitates "pivoting" motion by the laminitic horse, thereby easing his movements, in addition to providing the "full support" benefits of the egg/heart bar shoe line. Touted by some as the shoe of "last resort" or for horse owners who can afford the more expensive high tech heart-bar shoes. Of course, such a contraption can only obstruct the natural gaits and hoof-to-earth contact so essential for creating healthy hooves, as nature intended. *Avoid at all costs.* [Photo: ISNHCP Archives]

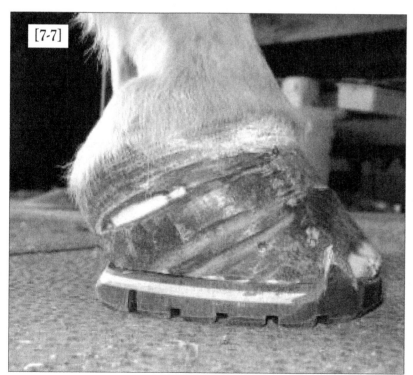

[7-7] *Grooving.* Grooving, sometimes called coronary grooving for its proximity to the coronary corium, has numerous objectives which have been explained to me in the field by its practitioners and horse owners: relieving pressure behind the hoof wall, stimulating new and improved growth, and mitigating hoof contraction are a few. Nevertheless, I have seen and dealt with the pernicious effects of this procedure in the field and can testify to its uselessness and dangers. Besides the reckless inhumanity, the reasons for doing it contrapose the fact that none of it is necessary in the first place. *Avoid at all costs.* [Photo: ISNHCP Archives]

[7-8a,b] *Wall resection.* The rationales behind wall resections, for which there are as many as there are variations of this invasive procedure, are as bogus, barbaric and dangerous as those advanced for coronary grooving. Who would do such a thing to a horse? The good news is that NHC science and practitioning mutes any advanced justification or defense for committing these high crimes of the horse world. *Avoid at all costs.* [Photos: ISNHCP Archives (*8a*) ; C. Pollitt (*8b*)]

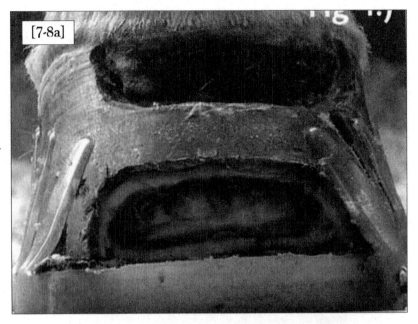

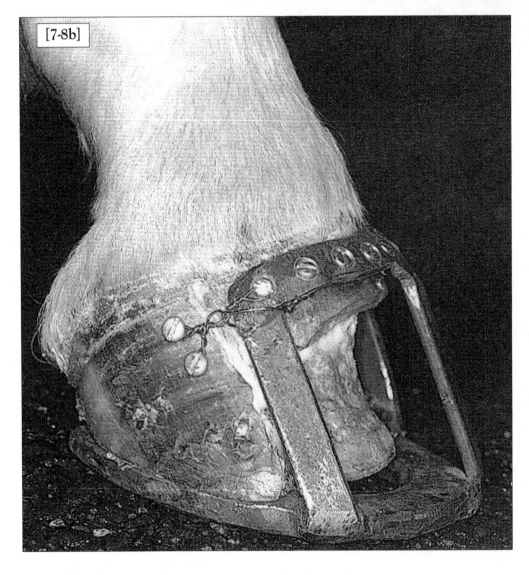

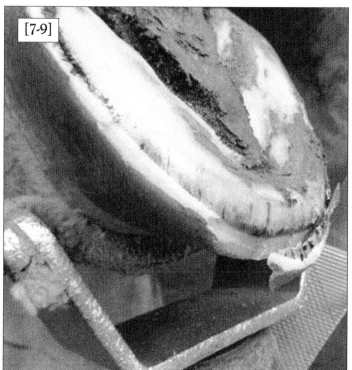

[7-9] *White line strategy "rehab" trim.* The premise of this popular invasive barefoot trim method is that by trimming the toe wall passive to the sole in the laminitic hoof (or any hoof according to its adherents, the LAM will be relieved of "sheer forces" tugging across the tenuous lamellar bridge due to the weight bearing force. The practice has its origin in farriery many years before the current barefoot revolution's inception. NHC science defines the trim as a wall resection. The argument against this practice is multifold: it is unnecessary, can obstruct or damage dermal processes active in the LAM, removes protective armor exposing or rendering hypersensitive dermal structures, provides microscopic or gross portals for pathogenic invasion from the environment, and removes wall necessary for support, thrust, and flight. *Avoid at all costs.* [Photo: ISNHCP Archives]

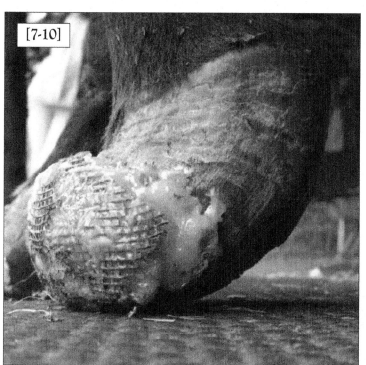

[7-10] *Tube trim.* I have no idea if there's actually a name for this trim, but I've seen enough of it to apply one myself: "tube trim". The hoof has been allowed to run amok – run under and wry in the very worst of ways – though I doubt from design than from not knowing what to do. In fact, this is a variation of the slipper toe hoof seen in Figure 4-10. The only possible reason I can surmise for sealing off the end of the toe with mesh and acrylic was to protect P3 or dermis following what might have been inadvertent over trimming of the "tube"? Clearly, these trimmers make a calculated effort to do something. Be that as it may, it is a wiser choice to supplant this enigma with a genuine natural trim. *Avoid at all costs.* [Photo: ISNHCP Archives]

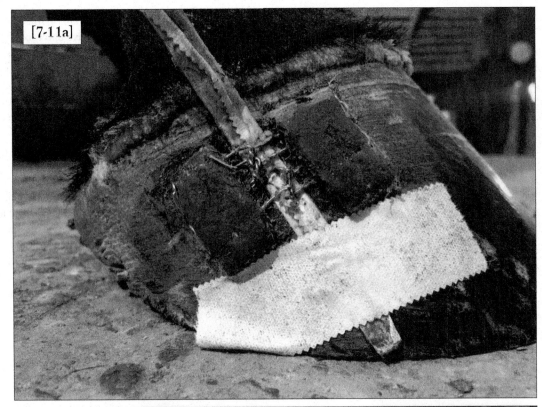

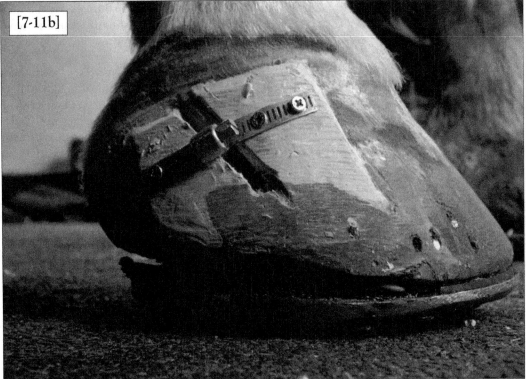

[7-11a,b,c,d,e] *Miscellaneous.* All of the images here depict efforts by professional farriers to deal with the consequences of chronic laminitis — principally "quarter cracks" and wall resections, all due to a weakened capsule caused by unnatural horse care practices. [Photos: M. Caldwell]

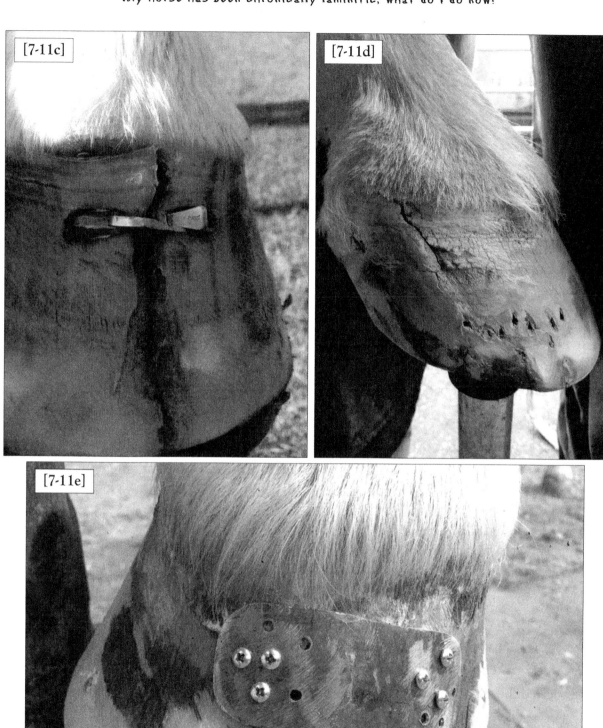

"My horse has chronic laminitis —
how do I Know if he has Navicular Syndrome too?"

Navicular Syndrome (NS), according to NHC science, is any severe trauma to the horse's body above the hoof that typically renders the horse unable to move naturally. It is characterized by two distinct symptoms — both of which must be present and identifiable to meet the NHC definition of NS: one of the front hooves is a "clubfoot", and the horse falters at the trot on just one of his leads.[1] A hoof is defined as clubbed if it measures 3 degrees or more than its paired front hoof, when both are trimmed to NHC guidelines for the natural trim (*Figure 8-1a,b*). As with chronic laminitis, many horses with NS are put down (euthanasia) because they are seemingly perpetually lame. I bring up NS in this discussion because some of the symptoms of NS overlap with those of laminitis, rendering a confirmed diagnosis of NS problematic if not impossible. And also because horses that are chronically laminitic and ridden are very vulnerable to NS "breakdown". In fact, it is common that horses confirmed to NS are also found to have laminitis — not because NS causes laminitis (it doesn't), but because horses unnaturally managed to one are often unnaturally managed to the other.

A complete discussion of NS pathophysiology lies outside the scope of this book, but has been taken up in one of my other books.[2] Of relevance here are the protocols for differentiating the symptoms of NS from those of laminitis, so that one can confirm a diagnosis of NS. These will require an evaluation of hoof angle and the horse moving at the trot.

The pathological effects of laminitis on the shape of the hoof (capsule) are quite varied but are discernable from NS — for example: the extent of white line separation; the presence and amount of blood in the white line; the extent (degrees) of P3-rotation and/or P3-penetration; whether the sole is concave, flat, or convex; whether the toe wall is slippered, "bull-nosed", or straight; whether the heel and quarters are contracted, run under, or flared; and to what extent and where (toe, quarters, heels) the hoof is sloughing. Then there are other issues to factor that may have affected the shape of the hoof: how the hoof has been trimmed, if it was shod and how, and if neglect was involved.

(Continued on page 52)

---

[1] The conventional definition points to symptoms purportedly related to damage to the navicular bone and its bursa. The NHC position is that there is no damage to the navicular bone, its bursa, or any other structure in close proxmity or direct attachment such as the impar ligament and Deep Digital Flexor Tendon, respectively. However, if there has been a surgical invasion of the navicular bone or any internal structure of the foot, then the damage — in my experience — will be permanent and NHC identifies it as "surgically induced Navicular Syndrome". If the damage lies above the foot, lameness may or may not be observable or present. Two horses trimmed to NHC guidelines met the test for clubfoot had clubfeet, but they were otherwise clinically sound and rideable without faltering at the trot.

[2] J. Jackson, *The Natural Trim: Principles and Practice* (2012), pp. 238-243.

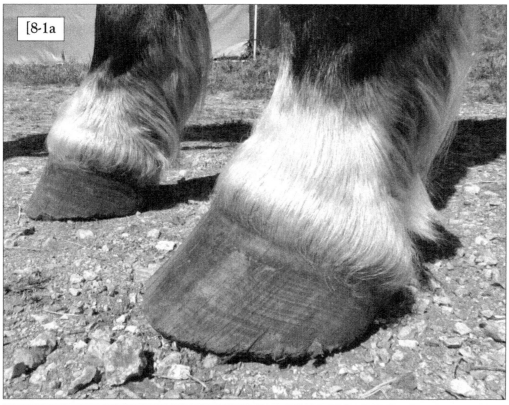

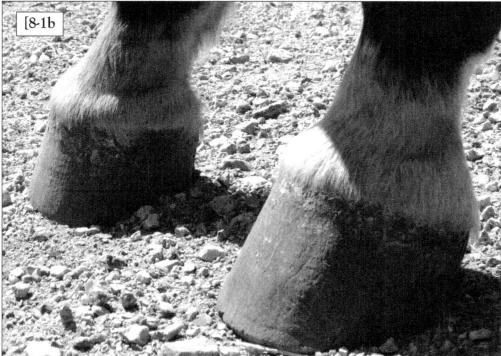

[8-1a,b] (*8a*) Laminitic hooves of a mare with the right front in clubfoot conformation — a signature of Navicular Syndrome. (*8b*) Five months later, NHC practices healed the laminitis, but the club foot remained. Nevertheless, she is sound two years into her life of NHC. [Photos: J. Willis]

Fortunately, distilling and differentiating the pernicious effects of laminitis on the hoof from a clubfoot is straightforward, although I recommend consulting with an AANHCP practitioner who has been trained to do this work. First, the symptoms of laminitis are diagnosed to confirm the disease (*Chapter 4, Figure 4-1*). Next, the hooves must be trimmed to NHC standards (the "natural trim"); in addition, hoof angle[1] must be gauged[2] and contrasted for both left and right front feet. The "test" for clubfoot is that the affected hoof must measure 3 degrees or more higher than the other front hoof when trimmed precisely to NHC guidelines. If the angle differential is less than this, or the same, then there is no diagnosis for NS. The test, however, should be conducted over a period of 6 or more months following a 4 to 6 week regimen of natural trims conducted by your qualified AANHCP practitioner. In this way, a hoof that has been previously rendered into an ersatz clubfoot conformation by an unnatural trimming method, will have time to recover and assume its natural shape or prove to be a true clubfoot, as the case may be.

The second test can be conducted once pain is brought under control through holistic management practices. If the horse is still sore-footed, the test is unreliable. The horse is evaluated at the trot, as follows, once foot pain has completely subsided: using a lunge line attached to a halter, trot the horse first to the left, then to the right, on a 60 foot (18 meters) diameter circle. My practice is to have the horse owner stand at the center while I follow just behind the horse with a lunging whip to provide impulsion to his movements. If the horse falters (limps) on either the left or right lead – but not both – then the diagnosis for NS is positive. But a horse that falters on both leads is not a confirmation of NS but is likely still hypersensitive due to damage to the LAM, and more healing time is necessary. The "trot test" should be conducted concurrent with the test for clubfoot following each of the natural trims over the same time frame.[3]

In conclusion, it is virtually impossible in most instances to diagnose NS with certainty in the laminitic horse as long as the feet are in pain due to inflammation of the LAM and the hooves are deformed, particularly those grossly so.

---

[1]Specifically, we measure the H° ("Healing Angle). See *The Natural Trim* (2012), Chapter 6, " The Healing Angle (H°) and Other Critical Measurements". pp. 97-125.

[2]H° is gauged with the "Hoof Meter Reader" (http://www.jaimejackson.com/products/hoof-meter-reader); a farrier's "hoof gauge" is unable to take this measurement because the hoof must be supported on a flat surface, not in hand.

[3]*Technical Note*: this test also relates to "crookedness", wherein the horse will tend to "fall in" (centripetally) on his "hollow" side towards the center; lunged in the opposite direction, he will "fall out" on his stiff side away (centrifugally) from the center. Horses unable to hold steady on the line in either lead are at high risk of NS if worked or competed to any kind of extreme.

Chapter Nine

Does Colic Cause Laminitis; Does Laminitis Cause Colic?

First off, what is colic? It is commonly understood to be a clinical (observable "pain") symptom of gastrointestinal distress. At other times it is used as a "generic term" to describe some sort of gastrointestinal distress. In any case, it is not a diagnosis based on a specified causality. In this respect, colic parallels the conventional definitions of Navicular Syndrome (NS) and laminitis, that is, the matrix of the pain/lameness is relegated to a spectrum of unproven or highly speculative possibilities with equally disparate therapeutic outcomes. According to mainstream reports, it is the number one cause of premature death in domestic horses. I have personally witnessed half a dozen deaths attributed to colic — all domestic horses. But not one in the wild — not to say that it doesn't happen, only that I haven't seen it in the Herd Management Areas I visited.

When conventional discussion moves to purported causes of colic, the subject becomes as complicated, murky, and contradictory as we see with mainstream ideas concerning NS and laminitis. For example, it is widely held that long strand coastal Bermuda has been implicated in ileac impaction, but at least one vet believes (based on veterinary hospital reports) spasms at the illeocecal valve, caused by potent fertilizers used to grow hay forage, cause the obstruction. But vets routinely give spasmolytic drugs in such colic cases, and horses still die. Growers I have queried —

who, of course, stand to profit from their Bermuda hay — weigh in to say, "No way, I've been selling it for years, and Bermuda hay is perfectly safe and nutritious for horses, and many horse owners swear by it as a safe, low sugar forage. I disagree with the vets' claims." On a simpler, perhaps more naïve level, if Bermuda is so implicated, why don't all horses colic from it? Whatever the case, as its asymmetric symptoms arise, corresponding causes are proffered based on those symptoms. To me, this is the stuff of specula-

Classic colic symptom — observable distress directed towards the hind gut. [Photo: Pixgood]

tion. Myriad other reasons for colic exist, from twisted guts, to gas overload, to infections, to impactions, on and on. Back and forth go the pro and con arguments, and, not surprisingly, "highly regarded" treatments in one instance fail in another. The veterinary community, from field vet to surgeon, tends to base their inferences directly on their experiences, what they "see" — and, predictably, their list of "reasons" and "treatments" is staggering — and can be very expensive.

The principal problem I have with all of this is the absence of any discussion about the horse's natural world and whether colic is prevalent or absent. Sadly, and as is the case with so many opinions regarding the "natural" health of the horse based on our wild horse model, there is no research. And no one is looking either.

But what about laminitis in all of this? *Does laminitis cause colic, and, conversely, does colic cause laminitis?* The two would appear to be related because the implications are that both laminitis and colic have diet as their respective epicenters. The question is bogus, however, because colic and laminitis are unequivocally symptoms, not causes. This book identifies causes or "triggers" for laminitis and how to deal with them successfully. NHC science and its corresponding practices are in concert on this, and holistic remedies are consistent with what we know about laminitis and the state of hooves in the wild based on credible research. On the other hand, the complete absence of any data or research regarding colic in wild horses of the U.S. Great Basin provides us with no vital information. *If the* diet, for example, lies at the bottom of the colic enigma, then research concerning the native diet and dietary behavior of wild horses would seem to be of paramount importance. The current rationale of treating colic "symptoms" as purported "causes" simply doesn't make any sense, other than as a "lazy" way of interpreting what is a potentially fatal problem. If colic doesn't occur in the wild, or at levels that are extremely rare in contrast to domestication, than the equine research sector is arguably practicing, if not defaulting, to willful neglect.

My personal hypothesis is that colic, laminitis, equine metabolic syndrome (EMS), Cushing's disease, and other metabolic breakdowns of the horse's body, are all symptomatic of what I described as the Whole Horse Inflammatory Disease (WHID) earlier in this book. This disease stems from dietary distress caused by putting things in horses — agricultural products, drugs, chemicals, and biological agents — nature never ever intended to happen. This would be consistent with my observations of wild horse populations and hoof studies at the BLM corrals where the symptoms of WHID are either non-existent or minimal at most. Since it is the premise of this book — based on my years of experience in the domestic field and in wild horse country — that laminitis is a symptom of this whole body disease (WHID) that is not confined to the hoof, are we remiss not to look once more to the digestive tract and ask, "Is colic —and other metabolic diseases of the horse — a consequence of intestinal and organ destruction caused by the same microbial pathogenesis leading to laminitis?" To me, logic favors this line of thought. But confirmation should come from the wild horse model and the cooperative efforts of veterinary surgeons, who must be perfectly clear about what they are seeing in the operating room or morgue, and vets in the field keeping track of horses that are diagnosed with laminitis (or have a history of chronic laminitis) and other metabolic symptoms of WHID.

Equine Cushing's disease [Pituitary pars intermedia dysfunction (PPID)] is conventionally diagnosed as an endocrine disease affecting the pituitary gland of horses. It is associated with a broad range of possible symptoms, including an abnormally long, wavy coat (called hirsutism) and, not surprisingly, chronic laminitis. In my opinion, Cushing's is a symptom of WHID, and, therefore, falls under the same NHC classification of symptoms as colic. [Photo: Abujoy]

For now, based on the evidence before us as I see it, it seems reasonable to say that whatever *causes* laminitis, probably also causes colic. For the horse owner who does not embrace NHC and is faced with the specter of colic, conventional "treatment" remains a "crap shoot" as long as cause is speculative, research findings are dubious or non-existent, and treatment is guesswork and unreliable. What is needed, needed badly, *and needed right now*, is research on what constitutes a naturally healthy diet among wild horses of the U.S. Great Basin. I am confident that the answer and solution to the enigma of the entire string of equine metabolic diseases lies there. With this information, we can then assert some rational perspective across the vast, speculative, and turbulent landscape of colic.

"Who do I go to for help with my laminitic horse?"

Chances are that if you're reading this book you are either dissatisfied with your hoof care professional, or your instincts have told you to look afield for better choices that are consistent with a belief that nature — what is natural to the horse — makes the most sense. NHC, of course, is all about what is naturally best for all horses. And there's no shortage of opportunities that you can take advantage of within the realm of NHC. It is regrettable that mainstream science and horse care has charted a course that neglects or clashes with nature's model based on the wild, free-roaming horse of the U.S. Great Basin and other similar biomes. The wild horse model has so much to offer to provide humane horse care. In fact, if you are going to go the "natural way", expect resistance from the general mainstream. No one who has embraced NHC hasn't felt the negative pressure coming from those who advocate and defend mainstream practices, including both service providers and horse owners. To hold your ground against the push-back that is sure to come, it is prudent to be confirmed in your own mind why you are taking the natural path. This means being educated about the species and the principles and practices of NHC.

There are several explanations that account for mainstream push-back and rejection of the natural way. Foremost, there is simple *ignorance*. Part of this is due to horse owners themselves who simply go along with conventional practices without questioning them. Most of these practices are rooted in traditions rather than a genuine understanding of the species, as well as a tendency to enable the veterinary world to treat symptoms rather than causality. Complicating matters further, such practices are often institutionalized and backed by bogus science that clearly fly in the face of what is good for the species based on their biology (i.e., the wild horse model). Indeed, this neglect of what's natural has taken an enormous toll on the horse, and in this assessment I am not alone solely as an AANHCP professional. Some of convention's foremost leaders have ardently gone public in recent years to decry what is terribly wrong. Readers already familiar with my previous works may recall the indictment by Walt Taylor, co-founder of the American Farriers Association, and a member of the World Farriers Association:

> Of the 122 million equines found around the world, no more than 10 percent are clinically sound. Some 10 percent (12.2 million) are clinically, completely and unusably lame. The remaining 80 percent (97.6 million) of these equines are somewhat lame . . . and could not pass a soundness evaluation or test. [American Farriers Journal, Nov./2000, v. 26, #6, p. 5.]

So, you see, one ought to be concerned about the professional advice and services they've been getting based on "conventional standards," and be wise to embrace genuine NHC practices that, in fact, cause none of the problems that those in the mainstream continue to create and defend

Hoof suffering from chronic laminitis turned into a complete "wreck" after being subjected to a bogus "natural" trim method. The hooves were finally restored after intervention by AANHCP practitioners. Any hoof not given a genuine natural trim based on the wild horse model can be rendered into a disaster no less than the "corrective shoeing" examples in Chapter 7. However, the most genuine natural trim cannot prevent a hoof from unraveling if the diet contains laminitis triggers. [Photo: J. Willis]

through default by doing the "same old thing."

Once one understands that ignorance of nature lies at the foundation of mainstream push-back, then one can really begin to appreciate how, at another level of complicity, it is reinforced by those *profiting* from such practices. Here, once again, I am referring to those behind the industrialization of laminitis (and, broadly, WHID) discussed in this book's introduction and elsewhere in its pages. These profiteers have been identified and published widely now on NHC social media and in our books, and you will discover them as you continue your journey on the NHC path. Briefly, these include the chemical and drug industries that benefit enormously from horses suffering from this disease. What horse owner doesn't have "Bute" or another NSAID in their tack room at one point in time or another? Well, these drugs are a billion dollar industry in their own right. As are vaccinations, and they have become increasingly routine, often given sev-

Promoting the AANHCP vital mission at EquiDay, Ermelo, Netherlands (April 9th, 2016); l/r: A. Gouw, ISNHCP SP; M. Schimmelpennink, Publisher *Paddock Paradise* (Dutch translation); M. Orbons, ISNHCP student; E. Van Nessen, ISNHCP student; B. Rhebergen, AANHCP Practitioner and ISNHCP Clinician.

eral times a year! Same with "de-wormers!" Behind the farrier industry we find corporations creating and pushing tools and equipment that really have no business being used on any living creature, let alone horses. Then there is the feed industry that has so many convinced that adding "free" sugars — known laminitis triggers — are safe. Feed companies, in turn, tie directly into agribusiness, the pharmaceutical companies, chemical industrialists, and even the university sector — the latter often financed to create, justify and lobby government bureaucrats to make corporate products "legal" and "mainstream". I could go on and on about the billions being made in the name of "safety". And don't forget that the horse world is a huge market today with many professional and corporate interests vying for billions of dollars of "disposable income".

But I will counter all of the above by saying that our model out there in wild horse country provides an immediate pathway to "vitality" and relative freedom from the laminitis industry. For AANHCP practitioners like myself, that is proof enough to go the "natural way." Having said this, it should be obvious by now that you should solicit the help of a qualified AANHCP practitioner if at all possible, because they can help steer you in the right direction and away from trouble and troublemakers. I'm sorry to say, you won't get that kind of support from your local vet or farrier, unless they are "closeted" NHC renegades! They are out there, but their numbers are pitifully few at this time and difficult to find among the phonies touting "natural this and that" to command attention, clients, and sales. The feed industry does have safe products, but winding your way to them through their myriad harmful products, pitchmen, sleek advertising, and seductive bogus science saying, "do all of these," can be daunting.

Instead, I advise horse owners to embrace the vital mission of the AANHCP:

> AANHCP vital mission is to advance the humane care and management of domestic equines worldwide through the application of proven practices and principles based on the research and findings of wild, free roaming equines living in the U.S. Great Basin.

Follow our protocols and recommended products to assure that your horse will receive safe, natural care. Later chapters and the *Resources* appendix will provide you with more information and important leads to pursue. And be assured that today, thousands of horse owners have taken the leap into NHC ahead of you. And, as we say, once you've taken that leap in all seriousness, there's no turning back!

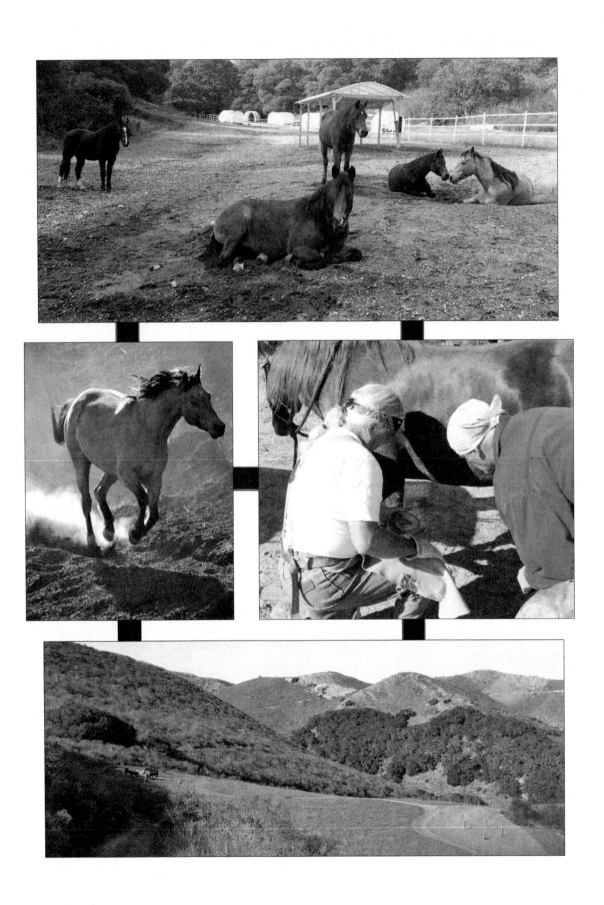

Preventing Laminitis: the 4 Pillars of NHC

The "4 Pillars of NHC" are the foundations for natural horse care, including prevention and rehabilitation of laminitic horses; hence, their central importance in this book. The 4 Pillars are *natural boarding, a reasonably natural diet, natural horsemanship, and the natural trim.* A comprehensive discussion of each of the 4 Pillars lies outside the scope of this book, but a brief summary is necessary to point you in the right direction if you are to "take command" of your pathway into NHC and facilitate their natural healing forces for the prevention or healing of laminitis. The *Resource* appendix provides additional important information and leads to aid you in your journey. Examples are provided in *Table 11-1.*

Foremost, the 4 Pillars of NHC represent a "whole horse", and, therefore, interdependent, system of care. For this reason, NHC is a true holistic method of horse care, including disease and lameness prevention and rehabilitation. Each pillar is defined and united with the others through the natural horse paradigm based on the NHC wild horse model. What does this mean exactly?

We would never say, for example, that riding a horse this way or that is natural to the horse, unless a reputable source has documented that the movements demanded by the rider also occur in the wild. Because without this substantiation, the meaning of natural can be anything, and with dire consequences for the horse. Similarly, we would not profess to know how to conduct a natural trim without knowing something about wild horse hooves. In short, being insistent and reliant upon the natural horse paradigm is a necessity, or the doors to "anything goes" in the name of "nature" would be opened wide, and the horse's true natural world — as a model — would be reduced to meaningless rubble, "words without meaning." While the tenets of NHC may seem purist and restrictive to some, they are also pragmatic and fair to both horse and rider. Here are four examples of how the pillars can work for you and your horse:

Natural boarding: Providing your horse with a more natural living environment will suit their physical and mental needs based on their species' adaptation as *Equus ferus caballus.* "Paddock Paradise" is such an environment because it mimics the home ranges of wild, free-roaming horses, and because it puts horses together to socialize in ways that are vitally important to their species. Your horse will become healthier for it — their movements, hooves, digestion, and psychological well-being.

A reasonably natural diet: Giving your horse a reasonably natural diet and feeding regimen will serve their digestive system and overall health, including laminitis healing and prevention. Like all other aspects of NHC, when we mimic the wild horse diet, the result is a healthier horse.

(Continued on page 63)

Table 11-1 Examples of the 4 Pillars of NHC*			
Pillar	Figure	Page	Example
Natural boarding	11-1	72-73	Tracking system
	11-2	74-75	Pathways & life on track
	11-3	76-77	Feed stations
	11-4	78	Watering behavior
	11-5	79	Mutual grooming behavior
	11-6	79	Sleeping & resting behaviors
Reasonably natural diet	11-7	80	Natural occurring minerals
	11-8	80	Digging for roots
	11-9	81	Hay bags
	11-10	81	Hay poles
Natural horsemanship	11-11	82-83	Moving in formations
	11-12	84	Prevention of lameness
Natural trim	11-13	85	Sand as abrader and polisher
	11-14	85	Abrasive tracks using gravel
	11-15	86	Close-up view of natural hoof
	11-16	87	NHC practitioners at work
	11-17	87	Natural trim in action

*All images taken at AANHCP Field Headquarters, Lompoc, CA, USA, unless otherwise noted.

(Continued from page 61)

Natural horsemanship: Riding your horse in ways that their movements are drawn directly from the natural gaits lies at the foundation of the NHC pillar of natural horsemanship. Obstructing the horse's natural gaits is a sure fire way to cause harm, such as Navicular Syndrome. The best way to learn how to become a natural rider is to observe closely and often how your horse moves and interacts with other horses in Paddock Paradise. Your horse will be your best teacher!

Natural trim: Having your horse's hooves trimmed to mimic the wear patterns of naturally shaped wild horse feet will help bring forth healthy natural growth patterns. Your horse will then be able to move more naturally because of it.

§

Okay, those are the 4 Pillars and the time has just about arrived to act on them and the NHC laminitis take action plan! But first, using the chart on the previous page, let's take a look at some examples of the 4 Pillars in a true natural boarding environment for the duration of this chapter. See you in *Chapter 12*!

[11-1] *Natural boarding.* Paddock Paradise is a tracking system modeled after the home ranges of wild, free-roaming horses. Paddock Paradise facilitates both sexes and all ages living together, while encouraging natu-

ral movement and natural behaviors 24/7. [Photo: J. Willis]

[11-2] *Natural boarding.* Paddock Paradise can be most any size or shape, but a central premise is to keep horses moving by means of stimuli seen in the horse's wild state. Feeding areas, watering holes/troughs, and

simple shelters all connected by meandering paths, encourage natural movements and behaviors. [Photo: J. Jackson]

[11-3] **Natural boarding.** Paddock Paradise, with its undulating, convoluted and interesting pathways that suit the equine species, clashes with the oppressive, close confining and segregated "box stall — square pad-

dock" and pasture "founder trap" lifestyles imposed on domesticated horses most everywhere. Photo: J. Jackson]

[11-4] *Natural boarding.* Given the opportunity, horses will drink water in which they are able to stand and wade, just as they do in the wild. Standing in mud below the water's surface is an excellent natural hoof cleanser and conditioner. [Photo: J. Jackson]

[11-5] *Natural boarding.* Mutual grooming is in nature an important daily feature of equine life in the wild — and also in Paddock Paradise! [Photo: J. Willis]

[11-6] *Natural boarding.* For a prey species, resting and sleeping together within the family band circle is all about security and a life free from the kind of unnatural anxiety that goes with isolation in conventional stalls and paddocks. [Photo: J. Willis]

[11-7]

[11-8]

[11-7] *Natural diet.* Paddock Paradise also facilitates horses seeking out naturally occurring minerals from rocks and other sources. [Photo: J. Willis]

[11-8] *Natural diet.* Digging for roots in Paddock Paradise. [Photo: J. Willis]

[11-9] *Natural diet.* Hay (net) bags are an important innovation in Paddock Paradise. Hay must be plucked from netting, simulating foraging behavior in the wild. As bags empty, horses will eat both "high" and "low" as also seen in the wild; horses will also pull a certain amount of hay from bags and eat it on the ground. Netting design prevents hay loss due to winds, and rain will drain from bags; it also prevents hay ruined from body wastes and trampling, a significant savings in money in the long term. Bags are hung from poles, which are easily moved along the track. Horses may eat from their own bags, or share with band mates — which is very common as seen here. This natural feeding system is effective in mitigating "food aggressive" behavior. [Photo: J. Jackson]

[11-10] *Natural diet.* Hay bags are suspended from hay poles with clips that swivel to prevent snags and catch points while the horse is eating. Hay bags attach in seconds with swivel clips. Pack and clip bags in your hay storage area, transport to feed stations for efficiency. [Photo: J. Jackson]

[11-11] *Natural horsemanship.* Paddock Paradise has demonstrated that horses move in "formations" based on relative dominance ("pecking order"), just as they do in the wild. Logically, horses should be

trained and ridden in groups in accordance with their natural relative dominance. [Photo: J. Willis]

[11-12] *Natural horsemanship.* Young 6 year old gelding galloping down a path in Paddock Paradise. Such a life does much to prevent lameness. [Photo: A. Gouw]

[11-13] *Natural trim.* A rolling area filled with sand in Paddock Paradise contributes to natural wear — abrading and polishing the hoof. [Photo: J. Willis]

[11-14] *Natural trim.* Tracks in Paddock Paradise should be abrasive. Countryside type gravel roads make the perfect footing to build strong hooves. [Photo: J. Willis]

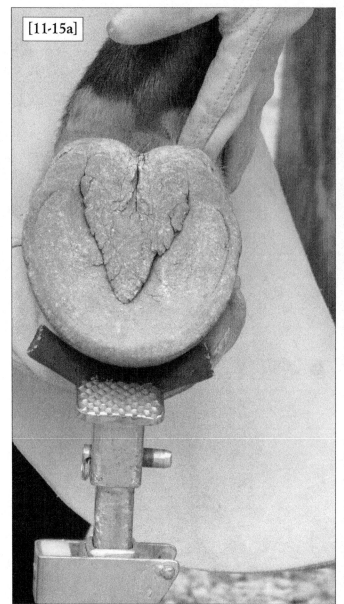

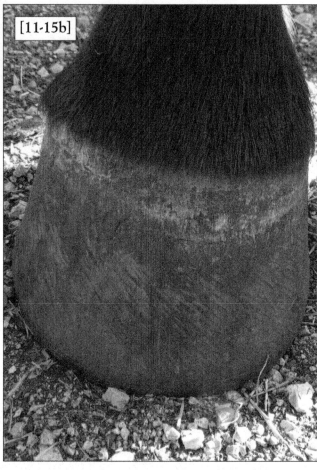

[11-15] *Natural Trim.* Close-up of exemplary naturally shaped (*a*) hind and (*b*) front hooves forged in Paddock Paradise. Both receive minimal — but very detailed — natural trims, which very closely approximate the wild horse hooves that I studied. What you see here should be the industry standard for all horses in all equestrian disciplines. [Photos: J. Willis]

[11-16] *Natural Trim.* NHC natural hoof care practitioners evaluate a hoof of a client horse for the natural trim. The science of natural hoof care is rooted deeply in the wild horse model. Years of academic and hands-on training are required to gain the knowledge and skills necessary to replicate the natural trim. [Photo: J. Willis]

[11-17] *Natural Trim.* Hind hoof trimmed according to natural trim guidelines and natural movements of the horse's limbs. [Photo: J. Willis]

[11-16]

[11-17

NHC Laminitis "Take Action Plan!"

This chapter is useful if your horse has been diagnosed with laminitis by your vet, or your horse is okay and you are interested in prevention of the disease. In either case, the "4 Pillars of NHC" will be your partner and guide in the effort. If you have a qualified AANHCP practitioner to work with, then your team has just expanded for the better! The "take action plan" explains the roles of each member of your team and what specifically each needs to do.

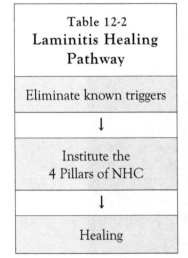

Table 12-1 Laminitis Causal Pathway (Simplified)
Any number of triggers
↓
Any number of symptoms
↓
Laminitis diagnosis

Table 12-2 Laminitis Healing Pathway
Eliminate known triggers
↓
Institute the 4 Pillars of NHC
↓
Healing

First, return to *Chapter 2* and take a few minutes to review the rather complicated schematic of laminitis causality in Table 2-1. Then take a look at *Table 12-1*. As you can see, this is a simplification of Table 2-1, but it's the bottom line – the triggers have culminated in a definite diagnosis of laminitis, whether it be the sub-clinical, clinical, or chronic stage of the disease. Table 12-2 delineates the "laminitis healing pathway" your team will follow. Our objective is to bring about nothing less than a complete healing. So, using Table 12-2 as our roadmap, let's get down to specifics so that we may heal or prevent the disease.

Eliminate the triggers

Getting rid of the triggers that cause laminitis is a surprisingly easy step to do, and I'm going to do my best to help you keep it that way. Here's all you have to do: simply stop doing everything you've been doing up until now! That's right, *stop it all*. Here's what has got to stop immediately: all medications, vaccinations, wormers, vet visits, possibly your farrier services, and probably everything you've been feeding your horse. As far as we're concerned, all of that has now come to an official end. Whatever those triggers and exacerbating practices were, we've stopped their flow and that's what's important right now.

And now that this is done, it's time to stop thinking about what those triggers were, or might have been, because it doesn't matter anymore. *They're history.* We have a saying in NHC, and I strongly advise to start thinking this way, "Ignore all pathology". Instead, think "vitality!" So, without another worrisome thought, let's move on to the world of NHC where we don't have those kinds of problems and we don't want them either.

With the triggers now out of the way, let's use the 4 Pillars of NHC as our new platform for action and take off from there! We'll start with diet, because what we're going to put in the horse will be the key pillar to halt or prevent any progression of laminitis and begin the healing process the natural, holistic way.

A reasonably natural diet

In all instances and all degrees and stages of laminitis, the starting point is always naturalizing the horse's diet. How soon does this happen? *Immediately!* Even if your horse is laying on the ground wearing bar shoes and is in excruciating pain. So, right where they're standing or laying — *right then and there* — take action and begin feeding our proven, safe NHC diet. The reason is this: laminitis won't let up with its death grip until the diet has been changed. What we're talking about here are taking steps to "naturalize" the biology of the horse's digestive system. The NHC diet acts probiotically and restoratively on the horse's colonies of digestive bacteria that are out of balance during laminitis. This imbalance, caused by substances we give to the horse that are toxic to their species' digestion, lies causally at the bottom of the pathological chain of events leading to laminitis and, I believe, all metabolic disorders (i.e., WHID). So, in healing or preventing damage to the horse's hooves, we are also doing the same to the whole body.

This is where the NHC Pillar of a "reasonably natural diet" comes in. It is based on my (and others) observations of feeding behaviors of wild horses and the types of things they eat in the high desert biome of the U.S. Great Basin. The NHC diet is modeled after these observations and is comprised principally of dry forage (grass hays), small amounts of chemical-free whole oats, and important micronutrients ideally fed in a Paddock Paradise type natural boarding environment. The *Resources* appendix of this book provides a link to the current AANHCP dietary recommendations which will explain what and how to feed your horse according to NHC protocols. These are exactly the same guidelines we follow in feeding the horses at the AANHCP Field Headquarters in Lompoc, CA, USA.

While you're learning about the NHC official dietary guidelines and locating the things to feed your horse, get your horse started on a grass hay such as Bermuda, Timothy, Orchard, Teff, or Brome, or better yet, a combination of them. If your horse is on a grass pasture, then it's time to take him off *immediately*. Grass pastures, as I discussed earlier in this book, are proven "founder traps." There is no known safe way to pasture horses. Internet "experts" who claim otherwise are leading you and your horse into such a trap. They have no accountability for what they say, so they can say anything they want, and they do. The ones brought to my attention by our vast audiences of dedicated horse owners clearly have no idea what they're talking about and could not describe the three stages of laminitis and their corresponding symptoms if they looked them in the face.

(Continued on page 84)

Horses eating "naturally" on track in the Paddock Paradise of the AANHCP Field Headquarters. They are kept out of the pasture at left by a single strand of electric fencing which has been turned over for more than a year! "Life on track," is natural to the horse as is the dry forage (hay) they are eating from hay bags suspended from posts. We keep five such feed stations on their track filled with a variety of safe hays 24/7. This simulates natural feeding behavior I observed during my wild horse studies. Increasing numbers of horse owners are now using hay bags to feed their horses hay based on the concept of Paddock Paradise. [Photo: J. Jackson]

Natural trim. Hooves here are suffering from stage 3 (chronic) laminitis. Such hooves require advanced training in the natural trim method. The horse here has been successfully rehabilitated with naturally shaped hooves, and is the subject of a 2 year study that will be published and which clearly demonstrates the "healing powers of nature" and the effectives of the natural trim, natural boarding, and a reasonably natural diet. [Photo: J. Willis]

(Continued from page 81)

The "natural trim"

Once the restorative influences of a reasonably natural diet and pain relief kick in, the hooves will probably need attention. The "natural trim" is recommended but it is very technical and requires highly specialized training to be conducted correctly according to strict NHC protocols. At this point in time, it is unlikely that either farriers, "generic" barefoot trimmers,[1] or vets are knowledgeable enough to do the natural trim according to NHC guidelines and probably won't understand the other NHC Pillars either. My advice is to work with a qualified AANHCP practitioner trained in trimming laminitic hooves.

Natural boarding

The only natural boarding environment I recommend, short of turning your horse out somewhere in the U.S. Great Basin with wild horses, is "Paddock Paradise". As was discussed in

---

[1]The descriptive "generic" is not to be taken as a slight, rather as a relatively meaningless, hence, generic term unless given definition, such as a methology. All "trimmers" should be able to explain what they are doing, why, what it is based on, and produce a body of horses that provides indisputable evidence that it is seminal in value. That's the NHC standard for the natural trim.

Natural boarding. Track life and terrain should be rigorous and challenging as it is at the Paddock Paradise, AANHCP Field Headquarters, the ideal environment for healing laminitis. Photo: J. Jackson]

Chapter 11 (and *Figures 11-1 – 11-6*), in "PP" horses move together in family type units along paths they create themselves (*above*), but inside what are called "tracks", which we create for them. Tracks are narrow passageways, on average from 10 to 15 feet wide, that circumscribe and/or crisscross someone's property. Tracks lead horses from one "event" to another, such as a feeding area to a watering hole. The purpose of the events is to elicit natural behavioral responses in the horses that favor their vitality. There is a growing international PP movement in the world today. Your job is to read the original text on the concept (see *Resources*), join the PP movement — for example, by following the Paddock Paradise Facebook page — and then see what you can to do to locate or create one for your own horse. Unless you have access to vast acreage in the high desert of the U.S. Great Basin, there is no better "healing field" in equine domesticity than Paddock Paradise.

Natural horsemanship

The key to understanding what genuine "natural horsemanship" is all about is to learn everything you can about the nature of the horse in his wild state. And, if you can create or otherwise board your horse in a Paddock Paradise, that's another excellent way to simply observe your horse in action with other horses and learn a lot about why and how he moves. You will learn nothing from horses in stalls except the true meaning of equine frustration, neurosis, and misery.

Equine paths in nature. *(Above, left)* A path worn by wild horses in the U.S. Great Basin. *(Right)* Path worn by horses living in Paddock Paradise at the AANHCP Field Headquarters, Lompoc, CA. [Photos: L. Gandini (U.S. Great Basin); J. Willis]

I would recommend that you read *The Natural Horse: Lessons from the Wild* (see *Resources*). Of relevance in this discussion is that riding a laminitic horse (or any lame horse) who is in pain or is still healing from damage to his LAM, is inhumane. *Don't do it.* It is tragic that many horse own-ers do ride their laminitic horses that are either under the effects of pain killers (NSAIDS) or are in pain, period. So common is this done that arguably it is an accepted practice in the horse world. To some extent, this is due to ignorance of laminitis symptoms, or worse, that it is simply because the horse can be ridden regardless of his problems. The right thing to do is to wait until you and your AANHCP practitioner agree that your horse is no longer in pain, healing has concluded, and he is ready to ride again without causing harm or using pain medications that conceal symptoms.

Action Plan for Clinical (Acute) Stage Laminitis

If your horse is suffering from an acute laminitis attack (clinical stage), I advise that you follow the schematic in *Table 13-1*. Very briefly, let's go through each of the steps, which, if acted on, will bring the attack under control. At that point, healing will follow by implementing the 4 Pillars of NHC just discussed. The following discussion explains the various steps in Table 13-1:

Call vet — First, call your vet to come see your horse for a diagnosis.

Diagnosis — This is important because you will need confirmation from your vet that the horse is laminitic and that it is at the clinical stage (*Chapter 6*) and possibly even chronic (*Chapter 7*).

NSAID — This is an anti-inflammatory drug (such as Bute or Banamine) the vet will prescribe. It will help mitigate inflammation and pain in the feet, which will bring the horse temporary (palliative) relief while healing. Tell the vet that you want an NSAID without added flavorings or sweeteners. *I advise against giving any other medications.*

Ice bath — After calling the vet, but before the vet arrives, I advise that you cold hose or, preferably, ice down your horse's hooves. If you have a small (child's size) swimming pool, or something comparable in size, fill it with water and stand him in it. Sensing relief, he'll want to stay there. Go to your local grocery store and buy half a dozen of the large bags of ice. If they have the solid blocks, that's even better, get those and put them into the water. Studies by the Australian Laminitis Research Unit (Queensland University) have shown that ice cold temperatures will quell the proliferation of enzymes responsible for destroying the LAM (*Chapter 1*).[1] This ice bath, in conjunction with the dietary intervention (discussed below), and possible NSAIDs prescribed by the vet, will help mitigate inflammation and pain in the feet, and bring the horse temporary (palliative) relief during his healing phase. Let him stand in the bath as long as he's comfortable, taking him out (if he'll go willingly, otherwise, leave him in there) for a few minutes every half hour or so to see how he's doing, but putting him right back in if he's obviously still in great pain. He'll let you know if he's had enough of the ice bath; you can also return him to it later.

Diet Consultation — There are several options here: use the consultation service referenced in *Resources*, consult with your AANHCP practitioner on site (see discussion *below*), or try using the AANHCP Official Diet Recommendations (also listed in *Resources*) on your own. You can also do all three. But, whichever, this is a necessary and urgent step to act on without delay.

---

[1]"Equine Laminitis: cryotherapy reduces the severity of lesions evaluated 7 days after experimental induction with oligofructose." A.W. Van Eps and C.C. Pollitt. Australian Equine Laminitis Research Unit, School of Veterinary Science, Faculty of Natural Resources Agriculture and Veterinary Science, The University of Queensland, St. Lucia, QLD 4072, Australia.

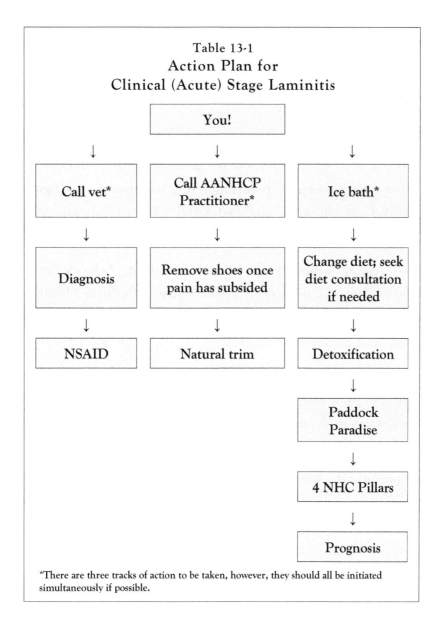

Detoxification — Feed any of the "safe" grass hays discussed Chapter 11 (p. 81). At the AANHCP Field Headquarters we feed Bermuda, Teff, and low sugar Orchard as the principal grass hays for establishing and stabilizing a healthful microbial balance in the hind gut. If these are not available in your area, then either use the consultation service in *Resources* to help you determine safe alternatives, or consult with an AANHCP practitioner in your area if there is one. Do not feed any of the grain hays (such as oat and wheat), or the legume clover, as these are also implicated as laminitis triggers. Alfalfa, also a legume, is used cautiously as a partial supplement in certified organic pelleted form for our one senior horse to aid in sustaining his weight. We have closely monitored him for sub-clinical symptoms of laminitis, and after several years there have been none. Otherwise, I do not recommend it for general feeding purposes without further studies to evidence its safety across a broader population of horses. Alfalfa pastures are a confirmed laminitis trigger, as is commercially fertilized and herbicide sprayed Alfalfa hay. In the absence of any evidence brought to my attention, I cannot confirm at this time if certified organically grown hay is safe for horses.

So treated, an acute attack should resolve within 24 to 48 hours. He may still have aching feet after that and not be able to move naturally, but the grueling, painful inflammatory response should be over. Horses suffering from P3-penetration (*Chapter 5*) or slough (*Figure 4-15*) are really medical emergencies and you will need a qualified AANHCP practitioner on site, or, at the very least, an NHC consultation (see *Resources*).

Paddock Paradise — Creating or moving your horse to an existing Paddock Paradise will serve two important purposes: first, it is an excellent environment to facilitate a healing; second, it is also the ideal place to prevent future attacks. Use the *Resources* to learn more about this revolutionary way to manage your horse.

AANHCP Practitioner — This person will, ideally, be your NHC "boots on the ground" expert to help keep you and your horse moving forward through the healing phase and on to long term prevention. Use the *Resource* to locate a practitioner near you.

Remove shoes — If your horse is wearing horseshoes, they will need to come off. This can be done by your NHC practitioner, farrier, or vet. I advise against doing this yourself if you've never done it before because it does require training and because damage to the hoof can be caused if pulled off the wrong way. It is generally not advisable to remove the shoes during an acute attack, both for safety reasons and because it is inhumane. My advice is to let the clinical stage pass, and then have the shoes removed.

Natural trim — Once the shoes are removed, any trimming ideally should be done by the AANHCP practitioner for the reasons explained earlier in this chapter.

Prognosis

As you can see, the 4 Pillars of NHC figure closely in every aspect of your horse's healing. Further, with the *Resources* provided in this book you'll have all the support you need to get the job done. What is the prognosis for a full recovery? If the 4 Pillars are faithfully implemented, I

What to Do If Your Horse Has Extreme Deformed Hooves

It may be that your horse has suffered from chronic laminitis, and if this is the case, and the hooves are extremely deformed, then your role will be to rigorously engage and sustain the 4 Pillars of NHC. The role of the NHC practitioner becomes very critical at this point. Extreme slipper toe deformity (e.g., *Figures 4-9* through *4-14*; image, *p. 84*), particularly if the horse has foundered (*Chapter 5*), will require execution of the NHC *Advanced Natural Trim Guidelines* to restore natural growth patterns. Not all AANHCP practitioners have received this specialized training, so be sure to query your practitioner to confirm they have, or email the AANHCP headquarters. Failure to use the advanced trim guidelines will likely result in "run away hooves," meaning the deformity will not improve and probably further deteriorate.

Hoof boots

My position is *not* to use them at all until your AANHCP practitioner has confirmed that your horse is sound enough to ride without them. As I've written earlier in this book in several places, if NSAIDS are responsibly given to the horse and the 4 Pillars of NHC are acted on with equal dedication, acute symptoms will conclude in days or weeks at the most. However, the horse should be sound without medications before riding; your practitioner will help you make this decision.

Other than neutralizing minor concussional forces during the hoof's support phase, hoof boots do relatively little to mitigate inflammation in the growth coria (dermata).[1] Until the triggers themselves are eliminated and the foot's dermal bonding mechanisms (e.g., LAM[2]) can begin to heal through detoxification, pain and deterioration of the hoof will only continue.

The argument that the horse needs boots because he must be *forced* to move or exercise in order to heal, or that he should wear them 24/7 until the feet are healed, is bogus. Moreover, some hoof care providers will argue that it is inhumane to ask horses with P3-rotation/penetration to go without boots or shoes. I once thought all of this myself, but the facts argue otherwise when one understands and brings to bear the 4 Pillars of our model.

---

[1]NHC science holds that the *concussional force* – trauma projecting into the foot from the ground (called the "support plane" or SP) when the hoof enters its support phase – is a minor force. The *compressional force*, in contrast, is derived from the horse's entire body mass acted upon by the gravitational field (G-force), and is defined as a major force. The latter is also referred to as the "weight bearing force" in NHC science when it is correlated to the "hoof mechanism". The NHC hoof mechanism is an extremely important model that explains hoof *form* and *function*; it is discussed at length in my book *The Natural Trim: Principles and Practice* (see *Resources*, p. 97).

[2]The LAM (lamellar attachment mechanism) is not the only dermal-epidermal "attachment mechanism" operative in the horse's foot. All of the foot's dermata (coria) are involved, hence: LAM, SAM (sole attachment mechanism), FAM (frog attachment mechanism), PAM (periople attachment mechanism), etc. NHC science treats all of these dermata singularly as an integrated "Super Corium". In fact, this is what I teach in the ISNHCP Training Program as the *Supercorium*. Accordingly, "laminitis" translates to "Supercoriitis," and the "LAM" translates to the "Supercorium Attachment Mechanism" (SAM$^\Sigma$). This is important because the myopic view that the LAM is the only attachment mechanism that is inflamed and deteriorating would be both misleading and incorrect. The most glaring example would be "hoof slough," a total failure of all the foot's attachment mechanisms (i.e., SAM$^\Sigma$).

Forcing a horse that is in great pain to move is simply inhumane, and having the horse wear the boots day in and day out for any reason, will weaken the hoof's epidermal armor and obstruct nature's healing mechanisms. In the case of the P3-rotation rationales, for example, my observation has been that the solar corium will proliferate an extraordinary amount of protective epidermal "plates" beneath the distal periphery of P3 in just a few hours if boots are withheld (*Figure 5-4*). Fitting boots — like shoes with pads — will only trap moisture in the epidermal solar dome. The sole needs to desiccate naturally via normal perspiration in order to heal and extrude sufficient numbers of dry solar plates to buffer the tip of P3 and seal off the underlying dermis from the environment. Applying tar (e.g., pine tar) and Halogen type desiccants/antiseptics such as Iodine and Chlorine to counter moisture, open the door to other problems we are wise to avoid — including blocking normal perspiration, destroying emerging healthy tissue cells, absorbing toxic chemicals, and obstructing dermis-to-ground communication channels to the foot's nerve bed that mediate natural growth patterns.

I *do* recommend boots for riding sound horses in environments to which the hooves are not conditioned. But this presumes also that the boots are not obstructing the horse's natural gaits or injuring sensitive tissues adjacent to the capsule (e.g., the coronet and/or skin above the coronet). And, of course, they are not being used as a way to mask clinical symptoms just so the owner can ride. Indeed, the entire premise of NHC is to restore and sustain the horse's vitality, not equip him by any means so he can be ridden or worked.

Afterword
"Wild Oats" for Horses?

This *afterword* concludes the current NHC strategies for dealing with Whole Horse Inflammatory Disease (WHID), and laminitis, in particular. The emphasis has been on restoring the native microbiology of the horse's digestive system through the principles and practices of natural horse care — the 4 Pillars of NHC. It is interesting to me that the NHC dietary emphasis parallels in some respects the late 19th century Victorian concerns about disease and human indigestion. The latter arose almost as an obsession, if not outright hysteria, because of the perceived impact and dangers of an emerging industrialized food chain. Scientists, physicians, patients, and the general populace alike all spoke out fearfully against what was happening — people were no longer eating "naturally" and "healthfully." One could argue that the modern "natural foods" movement began then — and with good reason![1] In fact, I personally share those same concerns today and am glad to see the emergence of the modern "organics food" movement. Because of organic farmers, ranchers, and processors, we have at least a little edge over industrialized foods that are chemically cooked, bound, and found everywhere. The good news is that more and more people around the planet want "safe food" organically and free-ranged produced, and new industries are arising everywhere to try and meet the demand. Although controversial and viewed with some skepticism by organic traditionalists, I've read that Wal-Mart, responding to over 90% of their food buying customers, is now investing to become the world's largest distributor of affordable organic foods in the world, under their brand name "Wild Oats". Sam Walton would have been proud! Hopefully, all in a good way for us, but maybe not so good for horses.

No one needs to be hysterical today to realize which way the industrial winds have blown into the lives of horses. Indeed, it's not good news. I've tried to make this perfectly clear throughout this book. Even Wal-Mart needs to focus here and make some additional adjustments, as their stores sell equine feeds laced with laminitis triggers. At the same time, I'm not one to whine about anything without offering up something to do about it that works. Of course, that would be the proven 4 Pillars of NHC. They work, there's good information available, and there are safe products for horses to consume to deal with their digestive diseases. Horse owners only need to get educated and then do something about it. So too the industrialists behind the problem and the many service providers down line who also profit from equine misery — maybe they should consider following Wal-Mart's lead. Meanwhile, WHID is still rampant, and laminitis remains an "epidemic of unconscionable proportions."

Jaime Jackson
Lompoc, CA
August/2016

[1] *How the Mid-Victorians Worked, Ate and Died.* Paul Clayton and Judith Rowbotham. Int J Environ Res Public Health. 2009 Mar; 6(3): 1235–1253. Published online 2009 Mar 20. doi: 10.3390/ijerph6031235. PMCID: PMC2672390

NHC Resources

www.jaimejackson.com

This is my website where you can find many links to the world of NHC, including tools and equipment for doing the natural trim, educational materials, training clinics, and my contact information. If your horse has laminitis and you're not sure what to do and need help, you may wish to start with my "whole horse consultation" to identify the causes and get you and your horse going down the natural path to a complete healing. This is also a triage service.

Diet Consultation (Jill Willis)
http://www.jaimejackson.com/pages/natural-diet-consult

Jill is my colleague and business partner in our work in the realm of NHC. Featured here is her diet consultation service. This is an important link because harmful diets lie at the very bottom of laminitis. Typically, horse owners use my NHC consultation to do the detective work to identify the laminitis triggers, after which I will send you to Jill to help you make the right dietary changes to facilitate the healing.

AANHCP Recommended Diet
(by Jill Willis)
http://www.jaimejackson.com/pages/natural-diet-consult

This is a monograph focusing on the specific diet recommended by the AANHCP. It is updated as new information becomes available.

Paddock Paradise Consultation (Jill Willis)
http://www.jaimejackson.com/pages/paddock-paradise-consultation

If you are in need of support for designing a Paddock Paradise (natural boarding model), then this is the right consultation choice for you. Jill conducts this service. Jill and I work closely together to manage the AANHCP field headquarters, which includes our association's Paddock Paradise, feeding program, and tours. Jill offers three Paddock Paradise consultations to horse owners: Planning and design email consultation, abbreviated "single issue" email consultation, and on site consultation.

www.AANHCP.net
Association for the Advancement of Natural Horse Care Practices
NHC Advocacy, Articles, Support, Links

This is the official website of the AANHCP. Here you will find a history of the organization, its legal status and vital mission, officers, NHC practitioners, and articles of interest. I created the AANHCP in 2000, and our members have pioneered the international natural horse care revolution ever since.

www.ISNHCP.net
Institute for the Study of Natural Horse Care Practices

This is the training arm of the AANHCP. There are two training programs for NHC professionals:

Natural Hoof Care Practitioner
Natural Horse Care Consultant

NHC Facebook Pages
AANHCP · ISNHCP · Paddock Paradise
J. Jackson NHC Services · The Natural Trim

The Natural Horse: Foundations fo Natural Horsemanship vividly describes how domestic horses can be made happier and healthier through an understanding of what nature intended for their species.

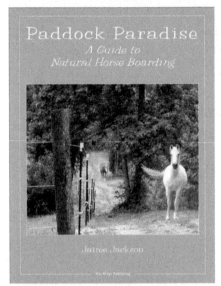

Paddock Paradise: A Guide to Natural Horse Boarding is a revolutionary model and guide for safe, natural horsekeeping, hoof care, and the healing and rehabilitation of lame horses. The premise of "Paddock Paradise" is to stimulate horses to behave and move naturally according to their instincts.

Founder: Prevention & Cure the Natural Way brings an entirely new perspective to the healing and prevention of laminitis. *Founder* assails the shadowy world of conventional veterinary therapies, and debunks the "founder mythology" which holds countless horses and their owners hostage to this terrifying malady of the modern horse world. This may be the most controversial book yet written on the subject . . . and the most useful.

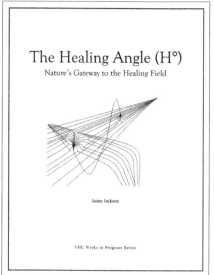

The Healing Angle (H°): Nature's Gateway to the Healing Field provides the historical backdrop for the cornerstone of the critical measurements, "H°". But it also takes the reader into the strange and mysterious Healing Field where mediation of mass and energy affects everything we do and life as we know it. It is an indispensable advanced companion addendum to *The Natural Trim: Principles and Practice*.

The Natural Trim: Principles and Practice is a comprehensive guide to the artful science of NHC. It is a textbook for the professional trimmer, as well as an important reference book for the horse owner wanting to understand the benefits of NHC.

AANHCP Field Guide to Natural Hoof Care was created to help horse owners understand how genuine natural horse care (NHC) works for the benefit of the horse, and what our responsibilities are to make it work.

97

About Jaime Jackson and the History of the AANHCP

The AANHCP came about gradually. In the 1970s, current AANHCP Executive Director Jaime Jackson was a practicing farrier. That experience revealed to him the many problems facing horses because of shoeing, unnatural boarding conditions, harmful diets, and riding practices that caused lameness. Jackson began to think more and more about what is genuinely natural and good for the horse based on his species's needs, rather than just what serves the special interests of their owners.

In early 1982, one of his clients in the San Francisco Bay Area adopted a wild horse in the new Bureau of Land Management (BLM) Adopt-A-Horse Program. Less than a week off the range, the hooves looked like nothing Jackson had ever seen or heard about before. There was only one thing for him to do ~ head into wild horse country to find out more. From then until 1986, Jackson returned again and again to the U.S. Great Basin to learn from America's wild, free-roaming horses and to study their hooves at the BLM's processing corrals near Litchfield (CA), Burns (OR), and Palomino Valley (NV). These years of investigation, study, and applying what he learned, laid the foundations for the natural horse care (NHC) movement we know today. By the end of the 1980s, Jackson ended his career as a farrier and became the world's first "NHC practitioner" and advocate of nature's model for humane horse care ~ the wild horse.

To share his vision for natural care, Jackson wrote his first book, *The Natural Horse – Lessons From the Wild*, published in 1992 by Northland Publishing. This led to numerous speaking engagements and invitations to write about his findings in many magazines, including the American Farriers Journal, which published over a dozen of his technical articles dealing with trim mechanics. As a result, during the 1990s, a trend towards general acceptance of "natural is best" for the horse came about. In fact, a new generation of "barefoot" trimmers soon followed. Many came from the ranks of horse owners who could not get their farriers to give their horses "natural trims". Today, it is generally recognized by NHC advocates that lameness issues, most caused or complicated by shoeing and unnatural boarding conditions, provided the main impetus for the skyrocketing interest in natural horse care.

Under Jackson's leadership, the "American Association of Natural Hoof Care Practitioners" (AANHCP ~ the forerunner of the current AANHCP) was formally organized in 2000. It was conceived with the primary objective of providing systematized hoof care training based on the wild horse model. In 2004, the AANHCP received its IRS designation as a 501c3 organization. However, by 2007, it was widely recognized that the AANHCP was more than just about the "hoof", but about every facet of the horse's life. It was also clear that membership and support for the AANHCP was international rather than solely U.S. based. The decision was then made to change the name of the organization to "Association for the Advancement of Natural Horse Care Practices", retaining the same acronym, "AANHCP". The association was re-incorporated in the State of California in 2008 under the new name.

Prior to early 2009, training of NHC practitioners was carried out under the aegis of the AANHCP. The ISNHCP was formed in mid-2009 to take over this responsibility, thereby relieving the AANHCP to concentrate on education and advocacy.

Today (2016), 34 years after Jackson entered wild horse country, the international natural care movement continues to expand to every corner of the horse using community, spreading its message that "natural is best" for all horses.

Image Credits

Abujoy - Own work, CC BY 3.0, https://commons.wikimedia.org/w/index.php?curid=32479940

Alessandro Brollo

Mark Caldwell

Richard Drewry

Luca Gandini (AANHCP)

Arno Gouw (ISNHCP)

ISNHCP Archives

Jaime Jackson (AANHCP/ISNHCP)

Grant Moon

Pixgood

Christopher Pollitt (Australian Laminitis Research Unit, Queensland University)

H. Ruthe, *Title page illustration from the German text, "Der Huf", 1959.*

Luke Tanner (AANHCP)

Aaron Thayne, *cover photo*

Jill Willis (AANHCP/ISNHCP)

Monique Wolfe (ISNHCP)

Roland Zhu

Index

CPSIA information can be obtained
at www.ICGtesting.com
Printed in the USA
BVOW07s1741150118

505280BV00007B/153/P